York Literary Review
2024

Spirit

Edited by *Chloe Bennison, Cat Boult, Ellen Dawson,
Jess Fisher, Kerry Holmes, Amie-Louise Matthews,
Amelia Rodgers, Rebecca Richardson* and *Megan Stoker*

First published in 2024 by Lendal Press
an imprint of Valley Press
Woodend, The Crescent, Scarborough, UK, YO11 2PW

ISBN 978-1-915606-47-1
Cat. no. LP0020

Printed and bound in Great Britain by
Imprint Digital, Upton Pyne, Exeter.

Contents

Foreword

"As I grow older, much older, I will experience many things, and I will hit rock bottom again and again. Again and again I will suffer; again and again I will get back on my feet. I will not be defeated. I won't let my spirit be destroyed." Banana Yoshimoto, *Kitchen*

On a chest of drawers in my living room sits a framed photograph of my Mum. I spent a long time trying to find the right picture, the need burning inside of me during the entire search. Then I found it. The perfect image to remember her. A moment which encapsulates her spirit.

It's from the early '90s, I think. I can't remember. The haircut gives it away though, her tight curls piled up on her head, an ancestral trait which I have inherited. Her smile is what warms *my* spirit every time. A sense of parental happiness eternally etched across her lips; her cheeks extended in a joyous grin. A glint in the eye. My early-teens self is in the picture too, dressed in neon-striped shell-suit, lying across her lap with my face in profile, my head turned in towards her body. A toddler-like embrace; momentarily free from all my burdens and thoughts. Just enjoying the moment. I am smiling too.

I don't remember when the photo was taken, but now it means everything.

My Mum is a spiritual presence. Her loss has not subsided and I find comfort in passing that picture every day. I can't help but smile, an infectious reaction radiating out from the framed image. When my spirit is low, Mum's spirit lifts me up and carries me on. Spirit is something supernatural, other worldly, but it is more than ghosts and spectres. It is quintessential to the human condition. Something that exists deep within and beckons us to carry on, reach out and connect. The spirit allows us the endure. It helps us to move past the hard times and realise that better days are to come. Spirit exists within and is evoked by memories – of togetherness, community, belonging, struggles and successes.

Welcome to the 2024 York Literary Review. The theme for this year's anthology is "spirit", chosen by the editorial team of postgraduate students studying the MA in Publishing at York St John University. The pieces gathered within this anthology have interpreted the theme in different ways, but the common thread is the tenacity of the human condition, the importance of spiritually belonging to something greater than your individual self, the need to experience the world around us and find connectivity. There are reflections on those lost, the struggles we face, joy in the little things and consideration of what makes us, ultimately, us. As Yoshimoto states, living means having to experience hardship and loss, but our spirit is what guides us to get back up and step forward again.

So, I beg you to turn the page. Read on. Experience the human spirit in all its guises. Maybe we will all learn something new about ourselves.

Dr Rob O'Connor
York St John University
May 2024

Preface

We are pleased to present the 2024 edition of the York Literary Review! This year our theme is "spirit", inspired by York's rich ecclesiastical and ghostly history. We are ecstatic about the range of submissions received this year, and the varying ways our contributors interpreted this theme; not only through classic ghost stories but also through communities from around the world, familial connections, love, grief and all things in between.

To the team, spirit also carries a variety of meanings. Chloe connects to the spirit of our inner selves through the determination, courage, and values we hold, and the way in which the experiences we go through create and nurture the spirit of humanity. For Cat, spirit is the essence of a person, place or period of life. The feeling of something familiar, whether that feeling is comforting or not. Ellen relates spirit to her community of friends. The inside jokes and mannerisms that bind them together and keeps them close after so many years.

Jess associates spirit with hope, light, and community. A community with a unified and spirited sense of togetherness has the power to create real change in a shared space. With two black belts to her name, Kerry interprets spirit as embodying the essence of Aikido and Bushido. A spirited discipline rooted in honour and loyalty; it means to harmonise with life's energy. For Amie-Louise, spirit means familial connections and forged communities. That is how spirit can bring us together as people.

Rebecca connects to spirit through her roots in the North. The beauty and terror of the gothic, as well as the sense of home and the people we associate it with. To Amelia, spirit is individual and personal. It helps us to progress both physically and mentally and makes us human. For Megan, spirit is synonymous with ephemerality. It means reflecting on unique experiences and the ways we are changed by them.

Inside this anthology is a selection of poems, flash fiction, short stories and creative non-fiction pieces that show just how varied "spirit" can be. From mythology to real-life experiences, our authors have shared their unique creativity and allowed us to put another exceptional edition of this review into the world.

Creating this anthology has been a spiritual experience in of itself; a way of community-making as well as a journey of gaining a deep understanding into the literature we produce. Small presses and anthologies are important. They create culture and meaning, whilst demonstrating the vitality and necessity of creative writing both here in the North-East of England but also across the world. Here, in the 2024 edition of York Literature Review, we hope to demonstrate how we have embodied all of these qualities but also fostered spirit of our own.

York Literary Review Team 2024

The Song of Dionysus

James Rance

the thirst is endless:
here on the sun-licked hillside,
here in a tangle of vines,
oils flowing from the crushed man,
blood flowing from the handful of fruit,
crushed
into the cup.

we have welcomed Him to this place,
danced to His flute and drums, torn
at our skin and the skins of others,
merciful, frenzied,
breathing the melody deep into our lungs,

the scalding red of fragrant wine awakening
us to the push and pull of the wind. our eyes have seen
the rippling furrows of thrice-ploughed barley fields,
                    the black finger of ergot,
                    the burning place which
                    is never burned,
                    the song of Dionysus.

we have pressed the fruits
between our hands and bled them into
the painted cup, pulled out
the entrails of the young bull
and stretched them over the flames,
called Him upon us:
> 'twice-born son,
> *thyrsus-bearer*,
> seize our limbs and
> dance upon the
> fertile earth.
> Come now, ivy-crowned lord!'

the light of the sun carves through a droplet
upon the altar, a ruby filled with fire,
and the Bacchic dance sweeps us to a distant place –
here in a tangle of vines,
here on the sun-licked hillside,
the thirst is endless.

Youth is Wasted on the Young

Anna Edwards

I am never taken seriously. But I like it that way. This is because when I laugh, I throw my head so far back you can see the metal fillings in my teeth, and I often stare into space and say the shopping item I forgot out loud much to the dismay of those sitting near me who think I can't catch side glancing at each other. I am straight to the point. If I can't hear someone, I say, 'speak up.' If I felt the bus driver had an attitude, I would call him a silly little boy. At bingo Doris won £50 so I asked her outright if she would be buying the rest of us a pint with her winnings. She did.

When I look in the mirror it shocks me every time. This doesn't really matter, though, because I don't have any mirrors in my house and looking at myself is the last thing on my list. I know I look fine. I don't recognise the woman standing there. I would think I was walking with slow elegance, the flâneuse of my town centre. This is the lifestyle I adopted. But in the Marks & Spencer window reflection I see a little white-haired lady shuffling forward in her outdoor slippers, because why would I not want my feet to be comfortable all of the time? A child once ran up to me near the park, mistaking me for their own Nana. I made myself laugh because I replied, 'If I was your nana, I wouldn't let you run around with sauce all around your mouth.' The mother apologised profusely. I spotted her soon after wrestling the child's mouth with a Kleenex the way all mothers do. When I got home, I did a painting because I wanted to, of flowers I had spotted in the newsagents earlier that morning. I painted them from memory so they would have been incorrect, but I thought the painting was fabulous, so I framed it and gave it to my friend the next day.

I wake up at seven o'clock every morning and I listen to the birds. There is a birdhouse right by my window that welcomes a different family every year. I sometimes speak to the birds about things that have amused me throughout the week. I think passersby assume I am mad, and I think this is hilarious, so I keep doing it. Every evening, I have my favourite dinner and I never look at the ingredients or the nutrients, I only care if it is delicious. I watch my favourite quiz show, and due to years of knowledge and life experience, I often get many questions right and do not have anyone tell me otherwise. The host is also easy on the eyes. If one of my favourite songs comes on when I am in public, I can't help tapping my foot along or even belting out a few lyrics, despite the fact I mostly get the words wrong. When Jean and I went out for a slice of cake and a cup of tea on Wednesday morning I sent our cakes back because they had cut one slice in half, as if to trick us, and they served us squirty cream instead of pouring cream. We got twice as much cake in the end and our drinks for free. On the way out I did a really loud burp.

In the winter, I decorate the house with tinsel and lights, and I keep boxes of biscuits in every room. I have an ornament of a dog near my doorstep that I have a little woollen hat for, that I knit myself, and he wears it in colder months. I hibernate and I relax, and I keep warm. In the summer, I wear my favourite dresses that are airy and decorated with flowers and fruit. I sit on park benches and let the sun drench my skin, every inch of it that it can touch, I let it fill me with warmth as I reflect on both my life and last night's fish and chips. I have been going to the same book club for three years and I always make sure that my opinion is known because my opinion is important, because it comes from my own mind and needs to be heard by others. When Darcy told us that the book we were reviewing was written by her granddaughter-in-law, I smiled and told her that was fabulous, but she needs to get better at checking historical accuracy when writing period pieces. Agatha then asked me afterward if I could read the short story she had been working on. I read it in one sitting that night and the next month I saw her I told her it was brilliant even though I had forgotten it mostly by then.

I wear the same perfume that I did when I was 30, because it reminds me of when I was pregnant with my now adult daughter.

It is musky and yellow, and I have often heard it being called dated and powdery by girls trying it on in the department stores. But it reminds me of a time when my body contained a life inside, the time it provided for two, and it felt such a strong new sense of love that it has never escaped me to this day. I carry that love with me always in the form of a few sprays on my wrist that I can smell whenever I move my arm to change the TV channel or when I lift my favourite biscuit to my lips.

When I sit in the park, I watch those around me. I think they assume I am sad because I am on my own, but I'm not. I am just relaxed, and I don't need various distractions and commotions anymore to engage me with life. I feel at ease. When I see children play, I am with them. The spirit of my 4-year-old self chases them with a stick. When I see a couple holding hands, I am with them, reminded of my own love that I have given and received, plentiful happy seeing it happen to others. I do not want to be the last one to experience it.

On one of the summer days, I sit in my purple and green floral dress that has lemons lined on the sleeves, and I watch a girl and a boy argue. She is pretty and truthfully, I do not care much to look at him. He shouts at her, and she shouts back, but I can see her lip quiver. She holds herself small and restricted. She is so young yet presents the confidence of a shadow. She has so much to look forward to, but her face again only sees the shadows cast on the ground by the huge green trees that only look like this a few months of the year. I see her crying, and after he leaves her, she checks her makeup in her compact mirror. She wipes the mascara from under her eyes and she leaves with shoulders hunched. I think, I wish I could put my spirit in her body, so she could experience it with the electricity of youth. But by the time she feels the same as me, she will be old like me too.

To a lover

Victoria Selnes

My bones don't lie here,
they're scattered in the tundra.
The curve of my skull
is soaking up untold history in
the soft marshland,
our sacrilegious marriage bed.

To drift off
to sea, a pair of legs the flotsam that
carries me. I don't care where I go,
aim the flaming arrow
on the water of Leith
or the Lethe.

At the edge of the world
I wrap my arms around
a great ash, or by luck a
cypress tree, fuel the ancient
memory, the branches that
softly shake me from slumber.

The earth swallowed me long
ago, I only got up when I felt her roots
tickle my neck. Uncovered in dirt
and moss I looked around and we
had a cup of coffee on the banks of
the Forth.

My bones don't lie here but if they
did, I'd dip my fingers in her
oblivious pool and whisper: «put
my dull beating heart
on ice, if you have some, and carve my
eyes into the crags

so when they dig me up
they'll only tear out a stem.»

Kaleidoscope

Jack Jackson

Tell me to look away when they're blinding,
but for all that you shed,
I cannot seem to split the glow of your eyes.

So, prove my point,
        my voice,
                my palm lines,

and despite only the knowing of it
I shall say the same things, over and over.
Warm them till they soften to paste.

And I will manipulate this
        into something better than words.

Who am I but Sappho, Longing for Divinity (Vignette #2)

Kummi Sandra

I still feel the music pulling me,
One beat at a time from my body.
The impertinence of my gaze
Catches up to me. I look down.

But then I've lost you, and I can't help but
Look for you all over again.
This time, you're not alone.

In the background, Sappho's spirit sings of a man,
Equal to the Gods
For, no Semele could look a Zeus in the eye,
And survive.

When that man turns out to be the Devil,
I see Kali in your eyes. The rage of a thousand suns,
The strength of Balarama, incorruptible.
The Devil leaves, defeated.

I see Ame-no-Uzume giggling over your shoulder.
'Dance for your August, your Amaterasu.'
But I am not the rise of your Sun.

Who am I but Sappho,
Longing for the Divinity to talk to you.

Sea Ears to the Ground

Ellen Harrold

It tangs and captures sunken sea matter,
the fallen debris reaching uneven floors.
It all sways.
Gossamer down.
For a blanket of spires
laying down roots for sunlight tangles,
moving back
and forth.
Under lunar tugs and tidal pulls,
rotting and skinning under the weight
of time and microbiomes.
Tread by *chluas mhara* larger than a lifetime of
rot. They shine in rainbow flecks and toxic
spillage,
but only upon violent evisceration.
The kelp provided them
with chemicals that make light shine
so gloriously beneath their backs.
Upon destruction, that brown plant matter makes
kaleidoscopes.

I drag the knife along their backs.

Word Meanings:
Chluas mhara = the Irish word for abalone and literally
translates to 'sea ear', referring to the ear-like shape of the
inside of an abalone shell.

Vox Clara Ecce Intonat

Elsie Taylor

Listen! A clear voice is singing:
'Night is through!' it starts to say;
'Wake up! as faint dawn blushes,
for soon begins a summer's day.'

Sweet it rings for August's star
that radiates with a youthful light;
A song of hope: 'Arise anew!'
conveyed through crimson-breast delight.

O! Tender is the song of praise
that peals from in a tangled briar;
Through slumber seeps this lilac lilt,
with each new verse a waxing choir.

Sing! Wren and Warbler, Finch and Dove:
'Here ends this listless hour!'
Dispel the dew that gathers, glints,
in new day's tear-dripped bower.

Listen! A choir of voices sings
in glory of the new-born sun which rises,
casts an unstained light;
to banish all that night has spun.

Beneath the fragile morning sky
ribbons of their voices float;
these threaded swirls of song appear,
on misted breath each silver note.

'Listen!' A clear voice pleads,
'For one day soon our song may cease.'
In morning, by the light of day,
a silent dawn shall bring no peace.

A Vegetal Consciousness

Sreelekha Chatterjee

Suki squirms restlessly on the tree branch. *How long will he have to wait?* The sun had set some time ago. A few hours before, he was down on the field outside the village where he intends to construct a factory, now covered all over with innumerable saplings. He never thought that clearing the verdure and getting the area ready would be an arduous task. First the trees were felled, and then the remaining vegetation was uprooted. A few days later when he ventured along with his team to initiate the work, he found the plot filled with countless saplings. It was the same every time he returned after eliminating them. This time the workers refused to deracinate the plants.

'It's a Jubokko, the vampire tree. Now it's coming after us.' One of the workers had told him, pointing to the nearest tree where Suki had climbed and settled now. He'd heard about the malevolent spirit trees in Japanese folklore that sustained on human blood. The seemingly innocuous tree is illusive, cloudily dreadful. Its branches are capable of gripping, clutching and pulling things inside. There is no question of astonishment if one finds human remains heaped at the base of the tree.

'It's the spirit of the tree that is responsible for creating these obstacles. We can't be wiping out the vegetal population, or else we'll be cursed.' They said before fleeing from the place.

Suki wonders who on earth can be behind all this.

A city-bred man like him, in his early thirties, refuses to consider these superstitious beliefs. While his mind is disturbed by these thoughts, he soon falls asleep on the branch. A faint noise from somewhere underneath stirs him to wakefulness. He peers into the sky that is awakening bit by bit with the east turning rosy. In the dim auroral glow, he sees 10-15 tweens carrying plantlets and establishing them randomly throughout the area. The dancing throng crowding beneath the tree fills the sky with a peal of merry laughter – decked with munificent splendour, bubbling with innocence, full of life and vitality like the young saplings in the plantation. Suki catches a glimpse of the little angels in between the gaps of the silvery green branches and dew-laden leaves, pouring warmth and radiance along the field.

Bewildered, Suki stares at them – eyes bulging out, mouth agape, beads of sweat accumulating on his forehead – while the tree prances around in the absence of wind. Slowly the children melt away in the verdant ground, amidst the grey of the breaking dawn transforming into a sea of blue. The last child dissolves into the surroundings, as the sun comes out with its magnificent, golden beams ready to shine upon the world. Gradually he sees his hands and feet transforming into foliage with heart-shaped leaves and long stalks jutting out. He feels the appendages of the tree forcefully entering his body, sucking his lifeblood. What remains of him is a swollen cadaver for the birds of prey.

Manhood

Ollie Groover

When I was a kid, my dad broke his finger
bowling. The pale flesh quickly turned purple
and swollen, puffing out on either side of his
wedding band. My mom wanted it to heal
properly so she asked him to go to the doctors.
He said she was being dramatic and insisted
on not making any sort of fuss so the matter
was put to rest. My dad's finger never healed
fully and now it clicks whenever he bends it.

My friend Zach died last week from a heart attack
after years of downplaying his recurring chest pain.
I wonder if his dad taught him not to make a fuss.

Harvey's Place

Laura Beddow

Snow sprinkled itself delicately over the pavements, a lace patchwork weaving between the cobbles of the street. A thin dust punctuated with scattered boot prints, markers of the person who once walked in them. Under the glow of a streetlight, a group of children chased the flakes as they hovered teasingly across their eye-line, clasping hands together to catch the precious spots before they melted into frost-bitten palms. A cluster of hats and scarves crowded together around a lit cigarette, passing it around and letting hot ash fall on the gravel at their feet. His name floated across the clouds of whispered breaths, secret keepers in long winter coats with hands made for pockets; warm words spoken softly into ears with stitched lips. '*Harvey Monroe is a wizard.*' Initial laughter from the listeners, but none from the speaker. '*I mean it. The man is a magician. Meet him, then tell me I'm wrong.*'

The sky was always dark when Harvey showed his face. Under the cover of nightfall he would brew his potions, shelves of glass bottles lining the walls. Some filled to the top, others keeping a firm grip on their last drops. Bottles on the top shelf wore jackets of thick, brown dust and held each other close with a net of cobweb connections. Further down vessels knocked together, familiar favourites piled in proximity. Harvey kept his tools close to his bench, never more than a stretched arm out of reach. He never worked alone, and the steady flow of customers helped to keep him busy. He had a solution to every ailment. Every lost job, every fractured romance could be glued back together by his gentle hand. He stored his magic at the bottom of every bottle, every tumbler, and every martini glass. Harvey Monroe laughed when people called him a "wizard", for his wizardry was just his work ... his life. They called his concoctions "potions", but really they were far more simple. No potions, just good, hard liquor.

Harvey seemed to like the spirits the best. So versatile, so easy to manipulate. There were few problems that couldn't be solved by a warming whisky or the harsh sting of a gin martini. Wiping a dampened cloth over the surface of his bar, Harvey let his gaze coat the room. The cellar he worked in wasn't glamorous in the slightest. The ceiling curved like an overturned narrowboat above, panelled with light wood and speckled with silver bolts. Booths of brown leather hugged the walls in the tight space; scattered chairs tucked under round tables where a few people chatted and chinked glasses. The room was cosy and intimate, but it was not the table lamps or strings of fairy lights that brought the warmth to the cellar. It was the hearty laugh of a businessman dropping in on the way home from work, the anxious, foot-tapping couple on a first date, the lovers in the far corner celebrating fifty years together. The cellar exuded a warmth so palpable it enveloped each and every visitor, soothing their red-tipped noses and numb fingers. At the top of it all was Harvey, the Master of the House, the loudest laugh and the friendliest smile. He said the best warmth was that of a Tennessee Honey whiskey, sliding down the throat and leaving behind an almost painful heat. His regulars disagreed. They came to Harvey's Place for the banter, the sarcastic quips followed closely by a cheeky chuckle. There were dozens of bars businessmen could flock to, and any number of restaurants adequate for a first date or anniversary. People came to Harvey's for *him*. The alcoholic alchemist. The man behind the martini.

I wasn't very old when I visited for the first time. It was a reward in childhood, a special treat for good behaviour. Mum liked it for the spirit – the inescapable air of positivity dripping from every surface. Dad liked it for the *spirits* – the gin, the vodka, the whiskey. Whatever he could get his hands on, it seemed. But they were both happy when they were at Harvey's. Everyone was. Drinks were cheap, and spirits flowed freely between customers. Strangers laughed like brothers: two straws in a shared cocktail. Few people left Harvey's Place without a story to tell or a new friend to tell it to.

As I grew older and more sceptical, I couldn't help but scrutinise Harvey Monroe every time I entered his establishment. I wandered in with a bowed head, hiding behind a cocktail glass while I watched him pour the drinks. Monroe was a marvel with a mixer, supplying his customers with a gripping performance as he danced with the cocktail shaker, tossing it up in the air and around his head--an alcoholic acrobat for all to see. The audience would erupt into applause, and eager hands would soon be filled with a chilled glass of his latest concoction. I kept out of trouble, becoming one with the shadowed corner. The passive observer, reducing my interactions to a watchful eye and a scrutinising sip.

It was like an infection. It changed something deep inside me, a flicking of a switch somewhere in the darkest depths of my soul. There had to be a reason that Harvey Monroe's name danced across the tongues of street-side whisperers. No one earned the nickname "wizard" on a whim. When my investigation began, I felt sure it was a secret ingredient. Generous measures, a higher percentage than other bars. Drunk people are happy people, and happy people spread the word. I felt sure that Harvey's Place was a breeding ground of fraudulent deceptions, double shots and smaller ice cubes. I watched intently from behind my half-empty glass, taking notes of quantities, the way he shook them together and strained them into glasses. I watched for close-up magic tricks, longer pours, and any way the bartender could possibly be spiking his own drinks. There was no way any old gin and tonic could live up to the praise the locals gave it.

That was the thing about Harvey's Place that nobody saw coming – least of all I. The more you drink, the more you laugh, regardless of the poison you pick. I noticed after a couple of struggled squints that not all of Harvey's bottles were alcoholic. The gin, the whiskey, the vodka ... variations of all three lay untouched on the top shelf, soldiers ready for a battle that would never come. I guess, in that respect, Harvey *was* a wizard. He made cocktails from orange juice and lemonade, fizzy drinks with edible glitter. When you went to Harvey's Place, you didn't need the sting of a tequila shot or the freshness of a cold beer. Grown-ups regressed to childhood, sipping their sparkly juice through bendy straws and shedding their hardened shells in time for happy hour. For it was *truly* a happy hour – not engineered by the contents of a bottle, but reanimated and brought to life by the long-forgotten smiles of youth.

I always thought he must spike his drinks, but really it was the opposite. Harvey Monroe kept his potions simple. A pseudo-shot, a smile, and a cocktail umbrella. He watched his guests – his *friends* – share a story and a cigarette under the fairy-lit cellar and he grinned. *'Everyone has a secret smile somewhere inside,'* he would say, when I asked. *'You just have to say the right words, mix the right ingredients, and wait for it to introduce itself.'*

Harvey's wasn't the only spirit in the cellar. But his was the only one that mattered.

The Jalebi Maker

Shamik Banerjee

Jalebis, ochreous, round and tiny, are aswim
In seething oil. The giant wok (whose rim's like tar)
Waits patiently to soak up all the yellow batter
Spiralling from the *lota* that's filled to the brim.
He takes this daily occupation as a matter
That calls for in-depth know-how. His mind and eyes are
Glued to the art. The ear splitting and constant chatter
Of crowds beside his shop imply they've come to him
To have this tantalising sweet. In the *bazaar,*
He is a luminary. People from afar,
However rich or poor, throng at his pastel, slim,
And antiquated store to revel in a platter
Of *chenna jalebis.* Although a megastar,
(he's been approached by auteurs for a feature film)
He scoffs at vainglory; if someone tries to flatter
Him, he says 'thank you', mannerly, wears the same dim-
Pink chambray, keeps the middle-parted, hot oil-spattered
coiffeur each day, and chews on betel leaves while hymn-
ing to Lord *Krishna* (this keeps his vigour unmarred).
I queried once, 'Where are you from, Sir?' in that clatter.
He kept the skimmer, spat the paan, washed up each limb,
And answered, '*Sitamarhi* district, Old *Bihar.*'

Word Meanings:
Jalebi = an Indian sweet dish
Lota = a pot
Bazaar = a marketplace
Chenna = unripened curd cheese
Krishna = a Goddess in Hindu Mythology
Paan = A flavoured betel leaf
Sitamarhi = a district (famous for its Jalebis) in the Indian state, Bihar
Bihar = a state in India.

Eventide

Alexander Lunn

It's true I cannot define many things
in this life. And I'm not a believer
that we can define what happens
in the next either.

I do know, however, a force
is ever present, something
unexplained that threatens cohesion,
challenges poetic articulation.

It darts away like a summer
dragonfly, or a glint caught
in the periphery of the eye –
a shape-shifting beauty.

I have given up the naïve
pursuit of trying to grasp it,
relaxed in my acceptance, not trying
to understand the incomprehensible.

Still, this energy commands.
Man maintains that they know it all,
yet it's wrong to think we have control,
I promise that's not nihilistic, just realistic.

What is this thing that makes us move
and dance? Perpetually a puppet-string
in all our lives. A warmth found
both in small doses or heady hits!

It sneaks in and wells up
inside, a feeling in flux,
half precipice – the rest an embrace.
Often causes mischief.
It makes me yearn to find
the place where the sky disappears
into the ocean and everything is alive
but also ending.

I want to stay there forever.

Can I just be held a little longer
in the grip of exhilaration?
Bathed in this power as the colours dance
blue, gold, white.

I find it wrong wanting to define
everything. We're not all that big,
and even if we think we are – there will always be
a greater spirit.

Five Weeks in Lišov, Slovakia

Eleanor Walker

Lišov (pronounced lee-show) is a small village in rural Slovakia, with a museum full of eclectic curiosities. I spent five weeks from August till September in this magical place as part of a placement alongside five other girls called Selina, Lily, Kris, Claire & Amy. Together we explored Slovakia and learnt traditional crafts and practices from local men and women.

The Beginning

It was night-time when we arrived in Lišov. As we drove down into the village along a road surrounded by fields and forest, I looked out of the window and saw the eyes of deer shining out from the edge of the woods. When I woke the next morning, I tiptoed outside to look out over the balcony. With warm stone beneath my bare feet, I saw the hills and the trees, so luscious and green, and I could feel the warm humid air all around me. Back inside the air was cooler, the house was big, echoey and eerie. We were staying in an old clergy residence and from then on, we called it "the priest house".

We spent the day exploring the village and museum. So many bugs! Different plants and trees! It was enchanting to be there. Wild and exciting, Lišov was like an oasis. Just walking for a little while, you could see river snakes swimming in the creek running through the middle of the village. Take a walk up into the forest and you might stumble upon ancient hidden cave houses in the hills, or find lizards basking in the sun on rocks back at the museum, home to old looms, traditional tools and masks from all over the world.

Power Tools and Eating Well

During the week we worked hard at the museum. Under the hot sun, I learnt how to drill and how to plaster a building using traditional methods and materials. To make the plaster, mix clay, straw, sand and water together and apply to the outside of a house. I learnt how to use a band saw and angle grinding became my new favourite thing. Coming from a city, it felt liberating having the freedom and time to learn through doing, in a safe space to fail and succeed in.

Every lunch time we were treated with delicious, traditional food cooked by Marta, a local woman from the village. Fluffy homemade donuts, hearty bean soups, strong coffee and tasty cakes filled our hearts as well as our bellies. Our host Jakub taught and cooked Slovak dishes like roasted vegetables and meat stews made in a clay oven. One night we made *Harula* (potato pancakes), outside over a fire. Later, we made small clay objects and animals, throwing them into the fire, eagerly waiting to find them partially fired in the ashes the next morning.

Wild Swiming and Wild Women

We went swimming a lot. In lakes and reservoirs with glistening cool waters, accompanied by lavender lemonade and Nutella pancakes. I used to be afraid of swimming in rivers, when I can't see what's beneath my feet, but it's a lot less scary when you do it with people you trust. I began to feel a familiarity and nostalgia for places I'd never been. Thinking about it now, I realise those feelings were probably because of who I was with, not the places I was going to.

On the new moon, we celebrated together outside on the balcony of the priest house, joined by a local cat we named Mamuška (pronounced mamushka, an affectionate term for mother), who visited us often. We spent the night talking, eating, listening to music, writing positive things down and setting them alight, hoping they would come true.

Teaching, Crafting, Connecting

We met many talented and kind people who weren't teachers in a professional sense but were teachers by nature. Everyone was unique but they shared an abundance of generosity, passion and humility. We met Miro first, who we considered a very wise man. When we met him, he was spending his days running a coffee and leather goods shop, using the proceeds to restore local cave houses in another small village called Brhlovce (bruh-hlov-ts-eh, but roll the 'r'!). Fero Liptak, an artist, had a great sense of humour and he invited us to create linocuts at his *Stodola*, a converted barn-studio. Soňa was a local weaver living in an old house that belonged to her grandparents, which she and her husband were restoring together. She had a magical garden, with peaches, apples and pear trees, dotted with flowers and bushes. We sat there with her in the strong heat of the afternoon, and she began to teach us what she knew. When we left, she gifted us a basket of fresh fruit and vegetables she had grown.

We would have many lessons with Soňa, but one stays clear in my memories. It was the morning and we sat in a small circle on blankets, in the grass of her tranquil garden learning about processing wool, from the freshly shorn fibre, to spinning it into yarn. This work, she told us, has always been considered "women's work" and it was a coincidence that we were an all-female group. After a quick eye roll at the sexist division of labour, we learnt that in the past, women would sit together carding the wool, telling stories and singing. As we did the same, a presence was felt, as if empowered by all the women who came before us.

Back to Nature, Myths and Stories

Between the power tools and hand weaving lessons, we learnt how to create baskets, with homegrown willow branches from another local woman called Tatiana who would also take us herb picking. We spent the morning wandering through the fields just outside of the village, identifying and taking notes about the properties of different plants and finding insects in the long grasses. Later that afternoon, we drank fresh herb tea with honey.

Slovakia was brimming with stories and folklore. Sometimes when I stopped to think about where I was it felt like I was living in one of those stories. In the town of Dudince (doo-din-tseh), there's a story of a beautiful fairy named Dudinka, who gave healing power to the natural springs found there. She is said to have healed a young boy who could not walk, and in the sloping hills outside of the wellness resorts, you can still find the ancient thermal baths said to have been carved into the landscape by the Romans.

One of the more mysterious stories is that of the "Wall of Giants". Today, all that's left are the remains of a large wall, overgrown with moss and oak trees, resembling nothing more than a small hill that you may not even notice you're standing on. Beneath the moss there is said to be volcanic rock and burned earth, but no one knows how either of these came to be there. Of course, there are many theories and myths: warring Gods; huge bones discovered close to the wall; the devil, because he always has a hand in the mysterious and unknown; volcanoes; dragons and even Icelandic legends. All of this speculation, but no one really knows the truth about how and why it's there. I think that's the beauty of it though, the reality of the why and how isn't there to stop the imagination. So, you can return to the child within you and run wild with the stories.

Goodbyes

Our flights left on different days, so on the last day it was only me and Selina. The evening before, we waved goodbye to the other girls we had spent over a month living with. It was the hardest goodbye I've ever felt. Selina and I woke early and walked to the museum for the last time. We went there to weave, with some grasses we had picked together a few days before, throwing the shuttle to-and-fro, the cloth grew. We cut our cloth off and tied the cotton back on, leaving the loom ready for whoever would weave next. As the sun was taking its place in the sky, we breathed in the morning air, saying goodbye to the village that had become our home, walking away with pieces of woven cloth in our hands and Slovakia in our hearts.

Ellis Bell

Emma Wells

Peudonyms offer a liberty of sorts – an inked nib stands readily poised to sign my manuscript: arduous yet fully loved is the toil of pages and fractious ink spill. My tattooed hands bear the mark of the literary industry: bleeding folds of unspoken words.

I pause deliberately. Second-guess myself whilst inky royal-blue globules drip onto crisp pages, hovering below my eye-line. A smudgy meeting, betwixt two integral components, is forged.

Charlotte signs so assuredly, swiftly, without conscious thought or self-correction. Robotic. Painstakingly verbose, not merely the soft, scratchy noise that emits from my quill: no voice given to its holder at all. As I like it. As I choose.

I cannot be exposed as Charlotte.

Writing poems was, and still is, an inner sanctum: sacrilegious, silent, life-surging. It is an eagle in full flight, talons navigating heaths below its spread wings, soaring on uplifts, marvelling upon wild meadow flowers; the shrews that tumble from plains of golden wheat – tasty treats to feast upon at twilight supper.

A public exploitation of our craft demeans us – a childhood venture commands privacy, privileged penmanship, protection. The worlds are ours. Not theirs. Not folly for the masses.

Glass Town, Angria and Gondal lie ransacked – peripheral castle walls demolished by prying, predatory eyes. Public disapproval washes upon fantastical coastlines, dulling waters, disturbing the natural ebb and flow. Too much exposure has bleached childhood colours from these microcosms, draining life from castles, forests and seas that we created in our canvas imaginations.

The once fictional, fragile beauty of our minuscule, fairytale worlds is lost, dissipating to dust in concrete hands. Tiny, bound books lie opened to the world – our calligraphy demurely fading thin, near to illegible with time's fading light.

She delved and devilishly demolished all inner peace that I had fretfully gathered beneath my feet.

She forced locks. Moved freshly inked parchments. Visual time prints of the moors shifted. My prized poetry now reeks of sabotaging hands. A slight against me. Unforgivable intrusion.

Hate the unravelling of secretive words, forms, exposed public screening and preening as if we are porcelain dolls upon a toyshop shelf to prod, assess, take as their own. Claiming literacy that they fail to understand. We are not dolls. 'No coward soul is mine', never echoed so strikingly in my thoughts as it does today.

A tawny, muted moor dweller cares not for gregarious greatness – let me merge, wholesomely instead, within unedited natural tones. Blend. Disappear in a raven's shadow as she clutches the moon, tumbling hedonistically in heather, romping with no abandon upon The Moors. A brown shrew of a woman, I am not for London and its limelight, and more pressingly, London is not for me.

Currer is brazen, progressively more so. Particles of London's hubbub have gripped onto the hems of her skirts, and she has brought metropolis grim and lacking morals back with her, sullying our clear, Yorkshire air.

How I miss her once quiet reserve. *Jane Eyre* has made her a household name. Damn her. Damn it. Each published page and embossed book cover. I hate any reference to Mr Rochester and his insipid Jane.

Rochester is now a fireside heartthrob: female readers swoon as they turn each seductive page. They long for such Byronic broodiness – a sultry solidity to hang their fleshy weakness upon. Finding only weakness in the husband that lays next to them as they try to twist the pages into being. This is what she loves about the masses: turning their thoughts to the bent of her own. Swooning over Mr Rochester's chiselled, well-worn attractiveness as greenish girls still brandishing childhood mittens.

Although, I find "she comes too short." Charlotte. Pernicious "pelican daughters" – this we are. The Bard captured and foretold our familial rivalry; we peck at each other's corpulent hearts, locked as one within the parsonage walls.

Regan and Goneril's venomous syntax echoes within our drawing room (Anne too pure to be included in my disparagement).

Competitive rivalry spurs our creativity – forces it to subliminally climb ...

Branwell stands not a chance. Let him paint himself out: dissipating in rivers of insobriety. He tumbles on waves of unconsciousness, laudanum heavy, drugged to inaction and ineptness.

Charlotte cares little for his forked fate. She ignores the Devil's calling at his sealed door. Each night he knocks more resoundingly than the preceding night before, his impatience growing by the very hour.

Give your readership what they seek: be bolder, braver, more Byronically bent.

I give the ravenous ravens my prize: Heathcliff.

Serve him very reluctantly to them on a platter under Charlotte's instruction and heavy duress.

His heathen heresy shocks and appals conservative readers.

Good.

Let their poised decorum squirm unsettlingly in fireside comfort. Hypocrisy laces, hanging itself upon each frigidly fingered page they turn. For this, my papery child, was never meant for them.

'This is a strange book', 'its plot is wild, confused, disjointed and improbable' compose the bulk of published reviews – coldly-iced criticism infringes my novel's sadistic sadness. Heathcliff chuckles at the disdain thrown upon him. Cares not for societal whims or views.

Is not love 'wild', 'confused', 'disjointed' and 'improbable'? They miss its poignantly honed, tightly held mirror of realistic reflections.

I care little for its fame. Instead, I turn my head to the wilderness of the moors: my solemnity, sanity ... salvation. My heartbeat home.

Heathcliff's wild spirit greets and toys respectfully, with my each, and every, adventurous step. His sheer recklessness emboldens and ignites my unconventional, muscular rage.

"I am Heathcliff" reverberates from each particle of cavernous heart space; wildness ensnares my footfalls; savage glances; barbaric inhalations of breath.

I scribble in frenzied circles, erasing the epitaph: 'Ellis Bell' upon the novel's cover (a first edition). With no hesitation, or dove-feathered timidity, I securely gouge, in deep set strokes: 'Emily Bronte' into its flesh with my conscious nib, painting, and securing, my own literary future.

Spiritus

Laura Autumn Cox

Incense burns and candles flicker. Supplicants gather beneath the thin dawn, with sleep draped around their shoulders. They stand in their chilled skin, eyes bright, lips parted, compelled to perform the ritual that permeates their lives.

The bell has beckoned them here, calling them to the Otherness.

The Otherness is unknowable, yet the supplicants feel the certainty of it in their hearts. It is beyond them, more than them, and they are indebted to it. The Otherness is like the sun rising into a pale autumn sky, chasing away the night. The supplicants cannot touch it, but they can feel its rays stroke their skin.

The wayward and lost are drawn to this place – this castle of memory, where the songs of ancient worshippers sing, still, in the stone. The heavy grey slabs are infused with whispered requests, laments, and prayers. The harlequin windows are portals into another, inner world.

There is a sound. It is the breath of gold-woven fabric sweeping across cold stone, and the gentle tap of footsteps muffled by the gilt robe. The supplicants lower their eyes. The conduit has come.

The supplicants believe that the conduit is an earthly channel for the Otherness, chosen to guide them through their wickedness towards blessed salvation. This is what the conduit has told them, and why would the conduit lie?

Lying is sinful. The supplicants know this to be true, for it is written in the time-worn book that only the conduit can read, the pages heavy with immemorial ink.

The conduit glides through the bowed-headed bodies and stops at the altar. It is engraved with eternal blooms, never wilting, never dying, frozen in stone. The conduit turns, hands folded like shy petals around a silken bud. The supplicants lift their chins from their chests, but they do not meet the milky eyes that wash over them. Those eyes see beyond the supplicants' adoring, mystified expressions to uncover guilt, pain, and desire. The supplicants are stripped of their pride, their misdemeanours magnified. They are naked, their secret sins screaming in the silence.

The conduit opens an age-lined mouth and speaks an incantation. *In nomine Patris, et Filii, et Spiritus Sancti.*

The strange language fills the space like sweet wine, and the supplicants drink it thirstily. It sustains them – for a moment, it dulls the ache of their hunger. For who are they, without the Otherness to weave words into the melody of their existence?

These words are the names that the conduit gives to the Otherness. And the words are powerful. They are words that have inspired fear, courage, madness, clarity, violence, love, war, and peace. The supplicants inhale the incantation and fall under its spell.

The Otherness has other names; more than can truly be known. It has been called life, death, surrender, faith, hope. It is all of these things at once, and more, for everything is sacred in its own way. It is the howling of the wind, the splash of summer rain, and the honied taste of harvest. It is the squirm of maggots in rotten flesh.

Guardians

Sharanya B

Social science text from middle school reads that in
Some village north of the country
women leaving
Their husbands and water pots
Chained around a banyan clinging their bodies
Against the trunk letting no axe graze
The wood without chopping their bones
Bangled hands clasping the bark
Their scarfed heads resting at it like a shoulder never offered
Like they had known already
That to save is to battle – to be standing erect
without a downward tilted face
without a coy smile
without rushing indoors at the sight of stranger men
But barefoot on the burning soil
Unslouched chests and vigilant eyes that fiercely warn
Nothing can be snatched
Even through the monochrome photograph
Down decades and decades
Like they had known already
The sweat of their bodies will water the
Saplings beneath into patches of green that spread
To gardens Spreading into thick forests
While the frictional heat from mehendi-stained
Fingers spark into a ring of fire
As they solder themselves into a goddess
They never had

This poem is based on the infamous 'Chipko Andolan' movement in 1973 when rural women from the state of Uttarakhand in India protested against felling of trees by hugging them as a chain, challenging the government policies on deforestation & felling of trees for commercial purposes in a non-violent way.

Bella's taking men to wych elm

Daisy Edwards

There's a girl in a tree up on the estate, did you
plant her there? Did you pry open the bark and set down the seed,
readjusting her bow and lace? I'm sure no one would miss her, that
   her voice is a raindrop in the tide of chaos in her home.
I'm sure she's just another mouth to feed, another set of teeth to
   clean, another
pair of ears to muffle when arguments boil over and spill under
   bedroom doors.

There's a woman in a tree, near the highest hill, did you stuff her in,
like your winter coat in the cupboard when summer arrived? Did you
push your weight into the bark, the soil, the wretched roots of it,
hoping no one would find your earth-soaked secret? I'm sure no one
   would notice because women go missing *all the time* these days;
they don't all get a newspaper headline.
I'm sure she had feelings about the gold ring on her finger, feelings
we'll never know,
you'll never know, feelings that are long rotted and forgotten.

There's a ghost in a tree, in a wych elm to be specific, did you
see her leading men there? All laced fingers and fish-hooked
   glances. Did you
see her pearlescent bones melt to flesh, muscle and sinew oh so
   tempting that even the married ones follow her. I'm sure they
   were just being friendly ...

It's nice to make new friends, isn't it?

It's nice to tell her to *cheer up, love* and *smile, sweetheart* and *where do
     you think you're going?* and *you look so much better when you* –

I'm sure there's a ghost taking men over the hills to a very specific
     wych elm.

There are men in a tree, creased into the valleys of the bark and
     knotted

up in the outstretched branches. Did you

notice how everyone acted when they left? When

they noticed their absence? Did you

see the breath we were collectively holding

because we no longer had to worry about it or try to fix it or talk to
     our friends and sons and colleagues and fathers about it? I'm sure
     these men

will be missed by their mothers and wives and daughters and sisters,
     and

I'm sure they don't know who the ghost belongs to. I'm sure they
     wouldn't know a man who would

fold a woman like laundry and tuck her into the belly of the wych elm.

I'm sure they would have spoken up.

I'm sure.

Mother! Mother!

Katie Day

When Mother died, little changed. I tended to the house, the garden. Performed my duties to the best of my ability. My senses heightened as ever, picking up small sounds and the signs of souls drifting by our front door. Mother never did lift a finger. Even when I was too small to work the stove or reach the cabinets. I was grown now, but preserving Mother's energies was still always of the utmost importance. So, it wasn't odd that I answered the door every day for a week after her death. That I went alone to buy milk. That the curtains remained drawn and no one saw a sniff of her. For all they knew, Mother was busy dealing with complex spiritual matters far beyond our mortal understanding. In truth, Mother sat down one day with her sherry and did not get up again. By the time I found her, she was gone. But that was none of their business.

The day after Mother's passing, I tried to get rid of the bad dream I was living. I wrote it down on a piece of paper, cleansed it with black tourmaline and set it on fire with one of Mother's best candles.

'Mother is not dead. Mother will come back.' I chanted. Nothing happened. Perhaps the spell will take time to work, I thought.

Until then, Mother's absence continued to tear through our home like a rabid dog. There was not a corner of the house where I did not feel her absence. Her velvet cape, hung up and waiting by the backdoor. A box of her favourite chocolates, unopened. These objects appeared to look up as I approached, then scowl with disappointment when they realised I was not her. The house itself was devoid of energy. Empty of her vibrations, her endless clattering, her barks of laughter. As though she had taken sound itself with her.

When Mother was silent it was a sign of one thing, a spirit had taken over. They always did pick the most inconvenient times to strike. *'The veil between this world and the next is thinnest when one is on the cusp of chaos'* she told me, sat on the kitchen floor watching me salvage our dinner, after a particularly lengthy possession. I'd found her chatting merrily to the spirit unaware of the gathering smoke and shrieking alarm. After that, I developed a keen sense for the arrival of spirits, anticipating it in Mother like a dog who could detect cancer. At a moment's notice, I could reach the other end of the cottage and keep Mother out of harm's way.

After Mother had been dead for three days and nights, I set about clearing her diary. I left Mother tucked up in her armchair, beside a vase of fresh tulips and locked myself in the study. Not that Mother would overhear. She couldn't. I knew that. But, what if she did hear me? What if the sound of her regulars' disappointment broke her heart? No, it was better to hide. Keep my voice low. 'I'm afraid there is *no* possibility of her seeing you next week. Or the next. No refunds either. Good day.' I thought that would put an end to it. That everyone might leave us alone while I waited for Mother's return. But the telephone kept ringing, at all hours of the day and night, until I pulled the plug.

Then, they began showing up. The day after the diary-clearing, I was outside clipping the hedges when Mrs Mackintosh came to call.

'Hello dear, is your Mother in?' she asked, creeping up on me with a cheeky *Thought I'd Just Drop By* look on her face. But the mask of politeness was thin. Worn by many others countless times before her. They appeared in many forms, some more forgivable than others. *Got Time for a Quick Seance?* was simple. A matter of *'Yes, Mother can see you at three'* or *'No, we're fully booked up until Christmas.'*

Others were more sinister. Vague. Hopeful. *Just Wondered If You'd Heard From My Late Husband Simon Yet?* Designed to twist my gut and let them in.

But, Mother's words returned to me, gave me strength. *'The world is an envious place my darling. When you possess great gifts, everyone wants a piece.'*

'I'm afraid Mother is terribly ill.'

'Really?' Mrs Mackintosh said, craning around me. I stepped forwards, escorted her back down the path.

'Yes. Violently ill actually. I've never seen diarrhoea quite like it.'

I decided to restrict my movements to the house and the back garden. Not leaving unless absolutely necessary. I plugged the telephone back in to prevent more uninvited visitors. My script evolved. Became tighter, meaner. Now, when it rang, I took a deep breath and said – 'I must ask that you stop calling, Mother really is quite unwell and for the last time, Derek she will not ask your wife where she keeps the dishwasher tablets.'

I even considered giving them the number of another medium, but then a chill crept up my spine, rattling my teeth in their sockets. With it, a gentle *shhhhhhh*, the sound of a mother soothing a baby.

Mother!

Perhaps this was a sign she was stirring.

When I was small, I had asked Mother whether she had been frightened the first time the spirits made contact. *'Not at all.'* she told me. *'The dead are always here with us, no different from you and me. The gift is simply a doorway. To possess the gift is to live in harmony with the spirit world. One day, you'll feel it too.'*

The thought of having the gift myself was nothing more than an absurd fancy. I tended to the books, supplied Mother with sparkling rosé and Turkish delight. Busied myself supporting her from a young age. This was how I came to know that Susie's parents were expecting when they bought a certain tonic from Mother. Rumours flew that I had the ability and I started to believe it too. That I could be like Mother. But, it came to nothing.

Mother had been dead for three weeks. The number of intrusions had dwindled, but so had the money. Without the gift myself, I could not hope to supplement our bank account. Even if I did have it, Mother's charm brought customers in. The way she carried messages from beyond the grave with such elegance, delivered them into the hands of the poor souls who washed up at our door. I remembered with a rush of feeling, a voice that had called through her the week before she passed.

'Derek,' it said, with the dry rasp of a smoker whose dedication has followed them into the next life, 'Derek, do not forget,' and she gasped, for even the freshest spirits can forget the living need to breathe, 'don't forget that it's Margaret's birthday next week.'

He wrung his hands and said, 'Thank you dear. And she's turning ... What? Must be eleven now – '

'Fifteen, Derek!' the spirit cried, with a power that would have knocked the wind out of another medium. But there she stayed, cutting an elegant figure on her chaise lounge. Poised as ever. You see, Mother cultivated the spirits' respect. Even the most passionate treated her with care. I hoped they were treating her with care now. Preparing to send her back to me. It was not Mother's time. Surely, they must know that.

Until she returned, I took care to maintain her physical form. I retouched her lipstick, wiped off crusted eyeliner and reapplied her signature swoop. I mopped her up daily and then almost hourly. I told her that I ought to get my baby's bib from the attic! How I laughed. I know Mother would have laughed too, if she could. I became desperate to throw open the windows and feel the air move, but I could not risk exposing Mother to the outside world. On a particularly dingy day, our home full of all manner of smells, I ventured out. Told Mother I was sorry, but that I could no longer survive on cans of tuna and gulps of air out of the bathroom window.

I hustled down to the corner shop, shrinking into myself like a shy tortoise. The further I was from Mother, the more wracked with guilt I was, until, trembling in the shop, my fingers slipped. I was so worked up that I did not notice the glass at my feet, the shards cloaked in milk. Did not notice the gathering crowd. Of neighbours, clients, buzzing with questions. I threw money on the counter and came home empty handed.

Only after I'd checked on Mother, did I attend to the pain in my heel, pulling out a shard the size of a penny. I doused the wound with a jar of seawater from our last visit to the beach. She always said the sea screamed to her, brimming with spirits as it was. What I would have given to see her throw herself into the waves again. Watch from my towel as it took her in its fist, swirls of spectral bodies tightening like a noose. It was often dark by the time they let go. But I did not worry, not when Mother seemed so at peace, so alive.

I was by her side when the doorbell rang. It was late. A dangerous time for a young woman to answer the door. I ignored it, fluffed Mother's pillow. Then, a shadow moved across us. In the corner of my eye, I saw black shapes pressed against the window.

They had come for her. Spirits or humans, it didn't matter. Everyone wanted a piece of her, didn't they? It wasn't enough to have her in life, they wanted her in death too. I should have known this would happen. In the grand game, she was only mine for a moment.

'Sandra? Dear?' came the voice of Mrs Mackintosh, 'we heard you've been unwell. We thought we'd come to check on you.' In the window, her nose and glasses came into view. Other faces I recognised too. They'd *unionised*. Come to cleave us apart.

I held onto Mother, hooked myself around her in a tight knot. Pulled a blanket over us. Refused to speak.

Eventually, they left, but it was only a matter of time before they came back. I untangled myself from Mother, dabbed at her with a fresh hanky and considered what to do when – from somewhere behind, came a voice.

Sweet girl. You've done so well.

It was clear, many layered. A choir resonating through my skull.

'Who are you?' I asked, no words leaving my mouth.

You know who we are. Bring her to us, there's not much time.

When I was a child, I'd had nightmares about Mother dying. On those nights, I'd crawl into her bed, bury myself in that warm animal scent and sleep a perfectly empty sleep. How she would laugh when she found me there in the morning, call me her little mouse and tell me what the spirits had said in her dreams.

When she died, I thought she was playing a trick on me. I pretended to leave the room and jumped back in to catch her off guard.

Now, I knew the truth.

Mother would never read my palm again. Trace the lines and tell me I had the world at my fingertips. She would never sleep-walk, put her keys in the fridge or drop coins in flowerpots. Never again would she swim to shore, shake off the spirits and come back to me.

The voices were gone now, but they weren't far. I could sense their magnetised pull, a cosmic tug in one direction. We didn't have much time, but they let me have a moment alone with her. I stroked the fuzz on Mother's cheek. Rested my head on her shoulder. Told her not to be afraid.

When it was time, I buttoned Mother's coat to her chin, waddled her to the car. I never did enjoy driving, but today I took pleasure in the open road, the smooth ride down to the shore. The sky was thinning, a slice of amber winking on the horizon. I told Mother everything would be okay. Held her tight. Pushed us forward. The tide came out to meet us like an old friend. Pinching at our ankles, thighs, waists. How eager it was. Taking us deeper now. Our coats soaked through, foam in our hair. Beyond the rocks, we lost our footing, Mother slipping beneath the surface, escaping my grip. I followed her under, tried to find her in the swirling abyss, but couldn't. My lungs begged to return to the surface, white spots appeared in my vision. I grasped for something, anything to hold onto.

Here.

Something closed in, held me. The spirits had arrived.

Don't take her yet, please. I'm not ready.

Something brushed my hand. Then came warmth, a body, pressed close. I held on, breathed her in. Said goodbye.

She Lingers

Lorraine Wood

You left it behind
Fully clothed
Draped across my chaise longue.
Face a witchery glow, a mother-of-pearl
aura, a tightly knitted, nipped-at-the-waist kind.
I felt your warmth, your nightly hugs when no one
was watching, as you sat at the bottom of my bed,

eyes on me.

I never felt you leave at first, you kept me close, catching
my every fall, cushioned by white, sometimes brown feathers.
As the days fell into each other, sideways crashing with every tear,
slipping notes inside my head, a song on my iPod shuffle, you danced with me.
You found things I had lost. Reminded me of things before I could forget, and all
the time, curving the memories, shaping them between your hands, you stayed
firmly with me, holding me up, never letting me slip away. Your spirit remains,
protecting me after 7 long years, replacing tears with fighting talk.
'You got this Fairy, you've got this'
A name I had not heard for years,

I have got this, haven't I.

Grandma's Bone Handle Corkscrew

Peter J Donnelly

She gave it away when she had a clear out,
but I'm unsure why she had it
in the first place, for there was never
wine on her table except once or twice
bubbly on Boxing Day. Once she had
a sip of red when she came to ours for dinner.
I'll never forget her face
as she struggled to swallow it.

She kept a bottle of sherry
in the fridge to offer her neighbour
a glass on Sunday mornings after church.
She'd go with choir to the pub
on Friday nights, and enjoyed there
at least one alcoholic drink
what of, I wasn't told. Maybe bitter
which she liked, *not by the half pint.*

Or a dram, like the one that cured
her sore throat on a visit to a Dumbarton
distillery. Perhaps a shot of Cointreau
as she did when toasting her late Aunt Edna.
Not I think, scrumpy, which her teetotal father
once got them both drunk on
during a hot walk in the Cotswolds.
He was, she said, as naive as his daughter.

Through the Eyes of a Child

Lucy Rumble

Once in a millennium, the gods grant their subjects a single wish.

At the start of time, they placed a single planet and a single tribe at the centre of the universe. They gave the tribe sufficient knowledge of this planet and their existence on it to make their first wish, and the tribe spoke as one: they wished for living things to keep them company. The gods gave them animals and trees. In the years following, the tribe began to grow, and when the time came to make their next wish, they were hungry for more. They wished for things to do, and the gods gave them jobs, hobbies and sports. New lands to explore and places to see. Diversity in land and colour and skin.

But the trouble started when things became too diverse. The tribe was spread too far, with too many things to do, that it was soon impossible to govern themselves as one. Their interests changed, cultures diverged, and the man chosen to give their wish spoke only for his own. The tribes that lived further out felt cheated and demanded a second wish. But the gods were gone, and so began the split.

Wishes became more selfish, more violent. War, weapons, and death. Last month, our time for redemption from this chaos arose again. One feels lucky to live in such a time of hope, but it's hard to feel optimistic when your neighbours are building bunkers underground. As expected, on the seventh hour of the allotted day, the clouds parted in the sky and a booming voice resonated throughout the earth. It said a name: Alya, the one who had been chosen, and announced that it would return the following day to grant their wish.

This was bad news, in my country at least. A non-white, non-male, non-adult, discovered in Egypt, had been chosen by fate, and she held our lives in her tiny palms. We made several attempts to reach her: we sent gifts and bribes, threats and promises, and dashing boys to steal her heart and make their fathers rich. But the girl paid them no attention: she rejected their material gifts, ones she likely had a hand in making, and laughed at the men in funny suits who came to talk in foreign sounds. The West had learnt too late that centuries of cruelty and abandonment could not be undone overnight. And so they grovelled, and begged, and cried at this little girl's feet as they realised in horror that it was now she who owned them.

Oh well. The men returned home, defeated, deciding to wait out this wish and work towards the next. But I knew nothing would change: time has shown that those non-receivers just foster hate, leading to further mistakes.

The following day, the world waited with bated breath for the child to ascend to the sky. As she reached the platform placed above her desert town, the voice bellowed once again. All cameras, all eyes, all hearts were set on her. She spoke. A short sentence. Followed by a pause. A great clap resounded through the skies and the clouds dispersed into pink fluff. She floated down, plucking candy from her seat and kicking her feet in glee.

Was that it?

For many, time stood still. They returned to work, deflated that their experience of this unique event had been rather unfulfilling, and resolved to fight for something better. That hope would drive them for a few years: societies would pop up, activists would campaign, but soon enough they would realise that they held no power over those unborn children of some future time. Our past mistakes had doomed us, and the best we could hope for was that the next person would wish for us to forget.

But, as it turned out, the pink clouds were just the start of that little girl's plans.

Murmurs floated in from the east that the east was developing at an alarming rate. The west had stifled all progress in the hopes of keeping them enslaved, but there was nothing they could do. Skyscrapers and complexes were springing from the earth in Egypt. Within the week, our differences were diminished, and the west was no longer an economic powerhouse. In fact, economics disappeared altogether. It seemed the girl had not liked mathematics, or exploitation – either way, money was gone for good. I half expected an old-fashioned bartering system to take its place, but perhaps that just shows my ignorance.

She eradicated the big players next: war, violence, famine, ill-health. Hospitals and dentists still existed. Much to my surprise I was called in for my check-up only to be told that my tumour was gone. They sent me home with a pat on the back and a lollipop. We were seeing the world through the eyes of a child, and it seemed her imagination had no bounds.

The best changes have been in the detail. How marvellous that a child should imagine a world with more butterflies! With glowing insects, fluttering like guiding stars against the night sky. The trees were thicker, fruits more plentiful, the air cleaner. But the strangest thing, aside from being able to walk without my knees flaring up, was that my hands were a tiny bit bigger. Larger, and more capable, I was stronger than I remembered – even before the chemo. And when I balled them into a fist, they tingled ever so slightly, as though they had plucked a positive charge from the air.

Now, for the first time in its recorded history, humanity is hopeful for the future, and the idea that someone might ascend those steps again, in the next millennium, and wish for something selfish … Well, that's simply out of the question.

As The World Falls Down

Holly Hartford

I still remember the day they told us. It was a Friday. I think I was having a good day. I think it was lunchtime. I can't remember what lessons I had, but I know I was in Law when they told us.

Everyone was mumbling in a bubble of excitement, consumed by the looming suspense. There was an announcement, they said. Everyone had to stay in school, they said; even those on their way home were told to come back. I remember Mr Richards saying *try not to worry.* He didn't say it was nothing serious. He didn't say it was nothing to worry about.

I remember going to my next lesson and sharing in the anticipation. Everyone was trying to solve the mystery. Miss Felix was taking the register and the boys kept asking questions, but she said she didn't know. I remember her looking over and giving me a sad smile. It was a *sad* smile, not a normal one. I remember saying, *something must be wrong, she gave me a sad smile.* It was going to be bad news.

It wasn't long before Dr Gibson came in. She looked so out of place in the classroom, alongside us mere mortals; she never came down here with the students. It must be serious.

She prefaced with something about how they'd all been crying that morning. And then she broke into tears herself. How strange, I remember thinking; I didn't think she could do that. Looking back now, it still feels as detached from me as it did in that moment. I assumed time would bring clarity, but some moments seem so drastically removed from reality that they simply cannot be interpreted. Perhaps this memory has stained because I cannot nibble at the edges and deface its truth; this past cannot be fully recovered, as it was never surrendered. I am there all the time, in that seat, hearing those words.

She pronounced it wrong when she said it, and I thought it

was someone else with the same surname, who I had somehow never heard of. But when they passed the letters around, I saw her name on the page, painfully foreign in that formal black font.

Last July, I turned nineteen. One year older than she was and will ever be now. It troubles me to think that she is stuck there, trapped in the past. All the rest of us, once younger than her, continue ageing and she does not. I can still see the placard in my photo album, her face, in loving memory. The pub after the memorial, when I left because we were all there without her. Outside the crematorium, bodies squeezed into crisp black suits, the yellow boots, the coffin, my apologies. Sorry for what? Over and over, *I'm so sorry this happened to you.* Shards of glass slice across my eyes. These visions are dusty but the colours never die. Perhaps it is not remembrance, but residency; scattered like ashes upon the smallest of details, she is always with me.

An early modern poet speaks something of a hearse, and I am thrust into flashing images of black horses and a carriage. I remembered the other girl, the one we didn't talk about, in the year above us when I was no older than nine. We didn't quite know what it all meant back then, but her parents had bought her anything she wanted for Christmas, even an iPad I had heard. I thought about how much I didn't want to leave, and how sad it was that she didn't have a choice. I remembered watching the procession go past. Mrs Kingston didn't stand with us. She probably didn't want us to see her cry. Later, I realise that children see a version of life that is filtered like a bitter hard-boiled sweet, sucked until the soft centre is exposed. It's easier that way, but as the years blink by, you realise that now it is your tongue that stings and you will never taste the centre again.

How funny it is, to read Rossetti and wince: struggling to breathe as Marvell solicits his Mistress. Perhaps tonight I will write that death happens to the living. This afterlife is mine.

Remembering appears to me as a portal, two mirrors facing each other. You can't look back and you can't look forwards; both directions are the same. I used to think of grief and its wrenching fist around my neck, but now I see who I used to be, and the person I'm becoming. Death is for the old, they said, and it waits for us after a long life. Now I know this was just another sugary centre fed to me by adults, by grown-ups, and guardians; the blanket of youth has slipped from my shoulders and there are no answers to my questions. More and more, I leave things behind, but this darkness ahead is cold, no longer illuminated by the shapes once drawn for me.

A memory is unmoving, but the lighting and its shadows shift with the seasons. As I watched the trees rupture into burning flames this November, that date crept up on me again like an infected wound. The earth has completed its course twice without her here, breathing, moving, thinking, feeling. This year, when I look back to that time, I mould its meaning like wet clay between my fingertips. I don't know what sculpture I will be left with, or how much carving it will take.

Perhaps this process never ends.

I know she is gone, but I have to keep reminding myself that she's never coming back; the spirit, the essence, is lingering still. Memory is something you wish you could shake off, almost like a jacket to hang up for another day. Instead, it forms like a skin over your own, entirely inseparable and never to leave again. And we see it forever in our peripheral vision; this is not something you can walk past on a meander through memory lane. The past has a beating heart and it is pounding in your chest, always.

(m)other courage

Peter Devonald

It requires courage to get up today.
It requires a leap of faith
to embrace the shadows.
Darkness dances all around you,
glimpses of words, memories, lost.

It requires bravery to know
there is so much you don't know
the distant lands grow further away,
language disintegrates softly with barely a sound
cracks appear where your life once was, longing.

It requires nerve to hold your head up high
as sinking sands grow deeper beneath you
sucking all your history into deeper black holes
swallowing your essence whole, souls weeping forlorn songs,
oceans passing, parting, meaning, flickering.

It requires spirit to still believe in sunrises
without skies flushed reds and purples,
magician's spell of rich palettes rewarded by warming skies,
photos and moments without context, names or reason
leaving you breathless, lost, alone.

It requires character to face the blankness
with embracing arms, to celebrate
what little you remember
fading, fading, fast, another weary day,
another dawn chorus, missed.

It requires acceptance
to be happy in this moment, this moment,
this moment, live forever in the now
to enjoy, endure, just be
blessed.

Mariner's Point

Grace Laidler

The brief read as it always did:
Female, 28, Mariner's Point.
Building blocks of stone-cold facts,
Constructing a case that chilled to the bone.

My partner drove us to the scene,
I let his phone direct him.
The window let the salty air in,
'Welcome to Mariner's Point.'

A seaside town nestled in the Northeast,
Pastel beach huts, twinkling amusements.
A little lighthouse overlooking the pier,
Guiding us to our destination.

The lighthouse should've towered over us,
But it screamed out for a lick of paint.
Yellow tape cautioned off the entrance,
Gleaming against the splatters of blood.

We ascended the rickety stairs,
Entered the gallery and there she was.
Slumped over the controls,
With her brains spilling out.

I wasn't a stranger to these sights,
But this struck at my core.
So I flew down the stairs,
And onto the sweeping sands.

The sea was calm and peaceful,
Just as I'd remembered it.
When I would collect seashells,
And play fetch with our dog.

I would always buy ice cream.
Vanilla, with strawberry sauce.
Monkey's blood, they called it,
It would drip all over my hands.

Mariner's Point was a postcard,
A place I remembered in snippets.
I took a piece of it with me at 18,
When I left for university.

But now it was gone.
Somewhere in that lighthouse,
Between the school trip and the crime scene,
It was Mariner's Point that took a piece of me.

The Bench on the Hill

Charlotte Tunks

Little Smeaton was a small village that lay in a valley of quiet comfort. Hills surrounded the town and kept the people safe from the harsh weather. On the highest peak sat a bench. It was wooden and painted white with care. It had watched the village of Little Smeaton for some time. Enough time to see the way it came together. The way the sweet essence of the village's spirit drifted up towards it.

The bench saw the leaves on the trees change colour, drift down and grow back. The bench had seen many things since its placement. Felt the hearts of the townsfolk, of the visitors and the wanderers. The bench had loved and lost and felt the love and the loss of all of those who sat upon it.

It had grieved and cried, prayed and pondered. The bench understood the people of Little Smeaton, perhaps better than the people of Little Smeaton understood themselves.

They were young. The couple. The girl sat while the boy stood fidgeting. The bench had seen enough proposals to know what was happening. He was nervous and the tension drifted from him to the bench's white paint, making it chip. At last, he pulled the ring from his pocket and asked the question. Joy flooded from the two of them and the bench held a little piece of their love within its wooden slats.

When the couple left that day, after joyous tears and loving kisses, the bench thought of the others. Those who had passed by and passed on.

There was a plaque on the bench. One for the name of Eliza Shortle. The bench did not know Eliza Shortle. Had never seen her or watched her while she sat. But the bench knew the man who often came just to sit. Weathered with age and wisdom, his fingers traced the name of Eliza Shortle.

The leaves fell once more and fewer people came to the bench on the hill. Sometimes there were groups of ramblers in their raincoats and walking shoes. School children hurrying home. When the sky got dark and the months got cold, the bench on the hill saw the twinkling of the lights. Little Smeaton settled in for the winter and the bench drew itself in for the long sleep. When the bench heard the rustling of rabbits it knew the leaves would be on trees again and there would be visitors again.

The man's fingers traced Eliza Shortle's name only once more before the bench felt the presence of Little Smeaton. People gathered themselves around the bench, circling it in sorrow. The plaque was replaced and the couple, now with gold bands on their fingers, placed flowers on the wooden slats of the bench. The bench felt their feelings. Felt the heartache and the despair. The bench worried for the people of Little Smeaton. It opened its arms to them, but they did not see. It wanted to share its seat with them, but they turned away and retreated down the hill.

The atmosphere of the valley changed after that day. A fog settled over the village of Little Smeaton and the bench could no longer feel the spirit of the town. It tried to peak through the clouds that shielded the valley but to no avail. The love that had settled in the bench was still present in the wooden slats that held it together. The bench only hoped that Little Smeaton still had something similar to hold it together.

Many seasons passed. The moon rose and fell. The sun shone and dimmed with each morning and night. Leaves changed colour, fell from their trees and grew back more times than the bench could count. The long sleep felt longer and longer until the bench could not differentiate between the sleeping seasons and the awake ones. The hill was barren despite the bench wishing for company. No one came. There were no visitors and the bench thought of the man with the time worn fingers and the name Eliza Shortle.

The lights of Little Smeaton glistened from below and the bench hoped they were well. The people in their homes had no wish to wander up the hill. No wish to watch the town from afar. Only to go about their days, letting the seasons pass without thought.

The bench opened its eyes to the sound of the grassy hill rustling. The long sleep had passed, and the rabbits were once again returning. There was giggling not far behind the rabbits and the sound of little legs chasing them. The bench did not know how long it had been since anyone had raced up the hill to visit, but nevertheless, the bench was delighted.

Following the brown rabbits that the bench often saw, was a small girl. She only looked old enough to have seen the leaves change colour and fall a few times, but her laugh echoed as she dashed after the rabbits. She was followed by the couple whose love still resided in the chipped paint of the bench.

They slowed as they approached and looked down at the bench with sorrow and shame. The bench saw them exchange looks and then watch how happy their child seemed. They stayed for a while. Sat on the bench with their child and told her stories of the place. They told her how they met on this hill, both sitting on the bench they sat on now. Told her how the man had asked the woman to marry him. How they had gathered to say goodbye to the man with the weathered fingers not long after saying goodbye to Eliza Shortle. They told her of them both, her grandparents. How Eliza Shortle had been the spirit of Little Smeaton. How the girl's grandfather had tried to keep her spirit alive. How that spirit now lived within her.

They sat a little while longer until the rabbits had gone, and the sky grew dark. The bench felt the loss of them after seeing them get smaller and smaller in the distance. The bench hoped that they would come back soon.

The bench did not have long to wait, for only a few sunrises later, they returned. The child chased the rabbits up the hill, followed by the couple. They carried planks of wood and the bench wondered what they had planned. More people followed and that feeling of delight returned within the bench.

The bench watched as the people of Little Smeaton built picnic tables from the wood they had brought. The morning was filled with laughter and hard work, and the people were filled with something the bench had not seen in a long time. Soon the tables were done, and the villagers celebrated by sharing food and stories of Eliza Shortle. The bench heard them, gathered them in its wooden slats, and nurtured them as if they were the woman herself.

Each month after, Little Smeaton gathered on the hill. They did not hide themselves away in their homes or distance themselves from each other. They came together as a community, to celebrate each other and those that were no longer. After the leaves had changed colour many times, fallen from the trees, and grown back, after many long sleeps and many celebrations, the girl with the spirit of Eliza Shortle inside her came to the bench on the hill. She took a finger, now weathered by age and wisdom, and she traced the names the bench had cherished.

To Exist

Brandon Shane

I never thought myself as gay,
or anything for that matter,
just a boy who loved,
had a right to love,
and my lips would meet his
on street corners, under lamplight,
inciting a sort of sacred rage
read in newspapers, studied in museums,
and my parents mourned this kiss
as if an imposter had replaced their son,
while boys kissed girls to indifference,
if not raucous applause. We thought
how wonderful it would be
to become ghosts,
wandering graveyards while others
danced in ballrooms. The privilege
of being left alone; bliss in hands
held without judgment,
and peace was always moments
from righteous indignation.
How I was willing to risk it all
in permanence
to be held again; along concrete,
or cherry blossoms yet
to be stripped of the last petal,
fighting for the right
to be human.

My Honest Poem

Sarah Illingsworth

I write from grotty places
throwing teacups at the ceiling.
A lot more breakdown before the build-up.

I buy fruit and let it rot in the bowl,
call it healthy and try again next time.

Everything I cook gets stuck to the pan.
I find it hard to touch the stoves
of anything I used to love.

I've given up trying to impress my dentist.
I'm too old for a sticker,
so where's the validation?

I try to reinvent myself once a week,
exchanging all of my piercings for tattoos
and I'm still nothing new.

I've become the breath in my mother's sigh.
Responsible for Jupiter's Red Spot
and most of her rage.

There's No Such Thing as C**'*

Elliott Scriven

For a split second each morning when my eyes flicker open, there is a moment where I pray that my circumstances before now have been one big nightmare. That in a seismic turn of events, I can rub my eye with my left hand or spring out of bed with legs that don't feel like lead. And every morning, my heart breaks without fail. What I pride myself on is that I always manage to put it back together.

'Good days and bad days are still days, they last 24 hours regardless.'

A motto I now try to live by. I think when I look back on my teenage years, that was the difference. I strung three or four bad days together at once. I don't recognise that Elliott now. Thankfully.

I have Cerebral Palsy. I don't have use of my left arm and I walk with a limp because my legs don't function as they should, as I want them to. Ever since I was young, a phrase has been religiously spewed at me:

'There's no such thing as *can't*.'

Even as a five or six-year-old boy, I used to laugh at the sheer absurdity of this statement.

I *can't* tie my shoelaces.

I *can't* zip my coat up.

I *can't* play a musical instrument.

I *can't* ride a bike.

I *can't* hold down stable relationships.

Maybe that last one is a bit of a stretch, though it certainly feels that way sometimes. I have a problem with relationships; whether that be romantically, with my parents, my family or my friends. My relationships all live on cliffs and I am in constant fear that they will get swept away.

That I will sweep them away.

I blame my Cerebral Palsy for this. It has given me not so much a chip on my shoulder but more an immovable rock that I have carried around like Atlas since I was an infant. I live in a permanent fear of commitment, abandonment, isolation. And yet, I have become a master of breaking my own heart. No matter how hard I try, I *can't* allow myself the thought that someone could love me for me. Someone who *can't* walk very far. Someone who *can't* cut up their own food. Someone who *can't* process what they are feeling.

I have just googled the difference between jealousy and envy. Resentment, that was the conclusion I came to. It has taken me until adulthood to realise that such feelings like resentment go hand in glove with my disability (well, my right hand at least). I know now that this doesn't make me a bad person. Do I hate that when I wake up each morning, my legs scream in pain? Absolutely. However, do I hate everyone who doesn't wake up with such difficulties? Absolutely not ... well, maybe not everyone.

Resentment is a multi-faceted issue though, as is physical disability itself. Everyone that knows me will tell you it takes a lot for me to get riled up. But when I do, I will fight tooth and nail for what I believe in. I'm the antithesis of a shrinking violet. One of my favourite qualities about myself is that I love people. I like to think I am kind, respectful, mature (when it suits) and dependable. Although, at the same time, I am not afraid to say what I think and I pride myself on doing it in as respectful a way as possible. Maybe it's the added perspective I have. The fact that I had to grow up so much quicker and earlier than my friends. Maybe it's that I got a peek behind the curtain of how the world works and its cruelties, as all disabled people do. Maybe, after spending so much time in the company of doctors and surgeons, I have stolen some of their forthrightness.

Whatever it is, it's authentic, and authenticity is a precious commodity these days. I have my Cerebral Palsy to thank for that.

I suppose that's something I'm jealous of – my disability always has to take precedent: Always. When I think back to my mid-to-late teens, the relentlessness of my Cerebral Palsy meant the reasons why I drank so much were not always healthy. I drank to forget my condition. But such a prominent thought isn't dispelled so easily, so when I had a beer, I'd have two or three or seven. I was drinking because I thought being good at it would stop people seeing the disabled person in the corner and more just a lad enjoying himself. One of them. I now realise that I was involved in a cycle. I was drinking to forget my disability. Then, I would become self-conscious of people's concerns about me, so I'd have another pint to help ignore that. And on, and on, and on. I'm glad that's not the case anymore. My liver is too. Although when I do drink, I still drink a fair bit, but it's always because I'm enjoying myself and the company I'm in, rather than to forget.

While at times my Cerebral Palsy causes my jealousy to become all encompassing, that's not to say I'm not thankful for my condition in many ways. It has shaped my personality and my outlook on life, often for better but sometimes for worse. I remember Josh asking if kinetics allowed it, would I have surgery to reduce the severity of my condition? I gave it some thought; I told him 'No'.

My disability is me and I am my disability.

It doesn't define me, but I can't say it hasn't made me who I am today. From my humour to my anxiety, my disability has become such an inherent part of me that if I were to take it away, I would cease to exist. Unfortunately, my disability brings out parts of myself I don't like. It has become my sword and shield, a wall for me to hide behind. A lot of my relationships fall apart because of my disability; it has given me anger that even at 24 I can't control at times. Luckily, this doesn't present itself in a physical or verbal anger. Rather that I shut down, and any attempt to break through is like a hammer to a tortoise shell.

I am jealous that the day I was born had such a monumental

bearing on my life. The fact that one extra knot in the umbilical cord, the extra 10, 20, 30 seconds without oxygen has cast a shadow over me that will never fade until I fade with it. Sometimes I ask myself whether it's worth carrying on through this blizzard of banality we call life. I have these intense waves of sadness, though perhaps they are more comparable to tsunamis. I suppose it's a kind of grief in some ways. Apparently, I grieve for what I lost that day. I'm not sure if I can grieve for something I can't remember having, I'm sure someone who's much smarter than I am can tell me. My disability made me and destroyed me all at once. I can't imagine my life without it; I can't imagine my personality without it. Perhaps, I would have been happier. Perhaps, I wouldn't have flirted with death as much as I have done. Perhaps, I wouldn't feel so lost or sad. Perhaps, I wouldn't feel the need to act as much as I do.

I have survivors' guilt about that, that Cerebral Palsy is essentially a lottery.

Some people's impairment isn't visible to the naked eye. Some people *cannot* talk or communicate with the ease that I can, if at all. Some *cannot* perform the most basic functions without assistance. Sometimes, I resent those better off than me. Other times, I feel like I can't complain without sounding like a twat, given all the things I am lucky enough to be able to do.

I can hold a conversation
I can dress myself in the morning
I can feed myself
I can go out with my friends
I can be independent

When I think about my birth, I feel conflicted. I like to think that once the most dangerous moments had passed, my parents were overjoyed to have me in the world at all. I know they were, but sometimes my mind wanders to the relief they must have felt at seeing me in one piece. I'm relieved that day worked out in the end, so I'm sure they were.

Even before I'd made my grand entrance, I was wreaking havoc. I refused to stay still. I like to think I was doing barrel rolls and front-flips when Nature decided to try and tame me by pulling the cord against me. It put up a fight, I'll give Nature that much, but I can't be tamed.

Not then, not now.

And yet I still feel conflicted. The negative side to that day was that I feel my fire was doused before it was given a chance to burn. I love the irony; Nature's device to transfer oxygen from mother to child is the reason I am what I am. The reason I am who I am. That day resulted in a trade-off being made. I got to, you know ... survive, and Nature took away the ability for me to walk in a straight line regardless of if I'm drunk or sober. If that wasn't enough, of all the things I could've grown up loving, it had to be football, cricket, music. Nature's idea of a great joke was to add a pinch of melancholy to all the hobbies I love. I wouldn't change liking them for the world, but I'm still waiting for the punchline to be funny.

To my light-skinned boy

Esta Innes

I don't want you to feel the need to have to pass for white,
to hide within the establishment knowing your ethnicity is out
  of sight,
you may not wear your identity overtly, unquestionably
but I want you to own your heritage proudly, unashamedly.
White, British-Asian, Hindu,
Scottish, Yorkshire lad,
but from a family that's all the same,
united in love, giving space for your dreams to begin
because your identity is so much more than your skin.

Your childhood will be filled with memories of magic
from both Christmas and *Diwali*,
eating fish and chips in Whitby, listening to stories
of my Gran-Gran and me,
then dancing with *Kaki* for *Navratri*.
You'll learn *Gujurati* with *Bapa*, play Playstation with *Kaka*
and have adventures in the Scottish borders with Nani and Papa.
Grandad will swing you to the park and back
then feed you *tatty scones*
to go with your Yorkshire puds, *dookra* and *popadoms*.

Me and Dadda won't shade you from the prejudice of the world
or pretend some won't judge,
acknowledging only part of you
but we'll navigate through,
by celebrating your fullness
and the tapestry of love that makes you, you.

I find myself again in Orkney

Rimika Solloway

'Would you like a drink, Rimika?'

The sing-song lilt of his voice when he said my foreign-sounding name had the quality of ambrosia. Now, I don't want to romanticise the way people are in faraway places because that might be called exoticisation – slurs which I often hurl at people who exoticize my culture Japan, the land of samurai and robots. Because yes, I do roll my eyes at them, those men who come up to me in public places and ask, *are you Japanese? Do you like anime?*

Yet I can't deny that where I find myself feels faraway and foreign. On a cold and windy isle, in the farthest flung corner of Britain where on a clear night it's possible to see the Merry Dancers – what they call the Aurora Borealis up here – as if the Latin name wasn't miraculous enough? I find myself again in Orkney. This is where I grew up from the age of six until eight. I was lucky enough to have lived here and back then, quite likely the only Japanese girl on the whole archipelago.

When walking out towards the sea or in fact anywhere on the isles there's always a strong wind at your back. Orkney is so relentlessly windy that no trees can grow here, even the shrubs have a hard time of it. One bright sunny day I was walking my scruffy little terrier ROLO on the crest of a hill looking out across the flat islands floating in the sea, when I spotted a shadow of a cloud amassing in the near distance. Within a few minutes huge hailstones started to pelt down from the sky. I ran around looking for shelter while covering my head with my coat, trying to shield my eyes. Of course there were no trees! So, I dashed to a barn and pushed myself up against the wall to seek protection in its awning while ROLO dove into a bush as we waited for the painful storm to pass.

The day I visited Ryan was no different from the rest, my coat lapels were flapping furiously even though all my buttons were done up. Looking up at the grey shale sky I saw a seagull flying stoically against the wind, stock-still as if it had been frozen in time. Burray Boat Yard read the plyboard sign on the large rectangular building painted dark green and vivid blue in the harbour. The backdrop to everything here was the sea.

'Would you like a drink, Rimika?'

'I'd love one. What are you having?'

Ryan speaks softly and slowly, 'Well, I rarely get to have a whiskey.'

'Then let's have whiskey.'

He comes back into the room holding a tray resting two tumblers of clear amber liquid. The tray is a dark shade of salmon pink with a gold trim. He carefully sets the drinks tray beside his well-worn armchair upon the windowsill that looks out at the wind-blown beauty of the island. He has a little brown dog with curious, wet black eyes like a seal. She trots up to Ryan and waits for him to get comfortable in his armchair. Then the little brown dog with the wagging cropped tail, lithely jumps up on his lap and curls up neatly to snooze. I look across the top of my tumbler of whiskey. It tastes clean and peaty. I gaze at Ryan, the old man of the island who sits in contentment with a furry croissant on his lap.

We talk about people we know in relation to one another. There is a man who lives up the road whose name he's forgotten, but he lives opposite the garage and next door to Wyn. *Do you know Wyn? I don't know, but what is it about this man?* He's opening a carpentry workshop in the building which used to hold the Post Office. He'll hire half a dozen men, they say, but there'll be no shop on the island anymore. A shame since there's no other place which sells newspapers. Ryan liked to walk to the shop every morning with his dog to get the papers and his daily dose of exercise.

Ryan's almost ninety now and so he had to write to the DVLA to renew his licence, but he couldn't get his eyes tested to prove his vision was still satisfactory because of the backlogs. On the list of official opticians supplied by the DVLA there's only one that's based on Orkney. This one optician named Tom has had to look into the eyes of every islander with a driving licence and the next nearest optician is in Inverness – 150 miles away.

Ryan walked into his opticians in Kirkwall and said to the shop clerk that he needed to see Tom.

The shop assistant said, 'Sorry, but he's booked up for months. You'll need to book an appointment online.'

But Ryan needed his eyes tested now. Otherwise, his driving licence would become void and islanders at his age need to be able to drive around to get to the shops – to have independence.

So he said, 'Tell him that Ryan Deerness is here, and he'll know who I mean. Tell him I need to see him now.'

The shop clerk went away and came back with a smile on her face, saying the optician would see him now.

Ryan's eyes were fine, he was able to pass the test and get his driver's licence renewed. He told me that Tom's father was his best friend before he passed away and he was pallbearer at his funeral, and so he had known Tom since he had been a bairn. That's how the island economy works on deep-rooted memories and good will, or bad will at that. If people don't know you, then they don't trust you. It takes a long while for a stranger to become part of the island community. My grandparents who arrived in Orkney in the 1970s are still considered outsiders, and to be honest, unless you're born and bred Orcadian three generations back you couldn't call yourself an islander.

We sat in silence for some time. Unheard of in cities where there's always some prat filling in a break in the conversation because they feel uncomfortable ... shared silence is deemed an attack on civic life. So, Ryan and I sit there for a while enjoying our whiskey, contemplating the island or maybe he doesn't because to him this is the everyday, the mundane. Whereas for me this is wilderness in all its raw beauty.

I believe time flows differently on the island. In the city where I'm from time ticks and each tick is an incessant itch at the back of your mind, you can't shut it out, only muffle it with bright lights and noises like explosions. But here on the island time stretches out all around you to infinity. The resounding sounds are of the waves breaking against shorelines and far out at sea, it's steady and reassuring, like an eternal exhalation of breath. What is an hour when it could be a day – what is a day when it could be a season?

I ask Ryan how he is doing. He says *fine, fine* his dog keeps him good company.

'Some people say she's got too fond of me. I don't believe 'em, but she does come *reet* back when I call her name *oot* there.'

I began stopping-in on Ryan during my walks around the island a few years ago for two reasons. One was because he has a terrier who looks just like ROLO and now, they are canine pals who roll around on the carpet floor together. The other was that soon after my mother died of cancer, Granny told me that Ryan's wife Tillie had also been diagnosed with cancer, so would I go and see them? I wasn't sure if my visit would be welcome considering what they must be going through and with my own grief stuck in my throat, but I went anyway and I'm glad that I did.

Ryan makes us tea and Tillie sits by me and tells me how she has a large tumour inside of her. She speaks fondly of how they have been married for fifty years and have had a good time of it. Every year they would take the motorhome down South for a summer holiday. They had seen all sorts of places, even getting to the Continent a few times as well, but mostly enjoyed the English seaside. Ryan tells me they're planning one last trip in the motorhome together, but that this time he would be doing all of the driving himself.

I feel a gush of awe brim over me, and I am the one asking for tissues. Neither of these epic old lovers who have stood the tests of time into their eighties seem afraid of facing up to the cold reality of death. In this final blow they do not flinch. I would have been clinging on to everything, but the pair are strong and resolved. They're made of mightier stuff up here, like the

Standing Stones, those Neolithic monuments made for the stars by the Ancients. Tillie says she is in pain a lot of the time but has decided not to take the drugs because they make her sicker and she was going to enjoy the last of what they had left.

When I walk up to the ruined kirk of St. Lawrence on the eastern side of Burray, the vast sea forever rolling in at its base, I read aloud the surnames carved on the tombstones in the lovingly maintained graveyard. The same family names repeat over and over again stretching back through centuries. Wylie, Ross, Towrie. Someone died in the 14th Century, and I see their ancestors crop up in the millennium, although the newer deceased are found down-wind in the graveyard furthest away from the sea.

I leave flowers on the graveside for Grancha who left Granny behind at eighty-six, their love still as pure as when they first met. I watch as the petals scatter in every direction with the wind like confetti. I stand by Tillie's tomb admiring the freshly cut engraving of her pretty name on the light-coloured polished stone. Then I walk on towards the edge of the cliff with the wind pushing behind me, with each step the graves getting more weather-beaten, the most ancient looking out over aeons of time across the North Sea.

The Holy Trinity

Claire Huya

Gripping the sanctuary pew,
Tears in my eyes,
A presence wraps me in their arms.

The weight is lifted,
A warmth blooms from my chest,
And I know that this is love.

My faith demands that I believe
A man in the sky I cannot see
Is the source of this compassion.

But these arms which hold me,
So familiar in their touch,
They must belong to my mother.

She's been there since the beginning,
Creating me in her own image.
Is that not a deity worthy of worship?

And when the time came,
Like the spotless sacrificial lamb,
She went quietly.

But even though she left this earth,
I still find her in the stars
Guiding me wherever I go.

I hear her whispers in the wind,
See her face in the mirror.
Oh, it is *beautiful* to be haunted.

To have my cries echoed,
Like she hears my grief
And makes it her own.

I love with her love,
Her wrath is my rage.
We are one in the same.

God was never there,
But my mother was.
And I *will* put my faith in her.

The Mother,
The Daughter,
And the Divine Feminine.

The Sisters of Spiritualism: Based on a True Story

Cheyenne Uustal

We didn't mean for it to go this far. I guess you can say that it was a series of unfortunate decisions. The first one was on the eve of April Fools when my sister and I showed Mother our abilities. It was just an innocent prank until one thing led to another, and it all became an elaborate hoax. A deception to the world; an April Fools gone wrong ... or right, depending on how you look at it. Suddenly, the Fox name was tarnished. I am aware now that I should take some accountability for that, and I do, but, at fourteen years old, how was I supposed to know better? I was excited by the success, the attention that came with it, and the community we were able to create.

We were The Fox Sisters – Leah, Catherine, and myself, Margaretta. Known worldwide, we were the most famous mediums of our age and the faces of Spiritualism. In a time when religion was rife, we were the ones that people turned to for comfort and answers about the mysteries of the afterlife. Everyone who came to see us was so desperate to believe that it was true, that their departed loved ones were really sending them messages from the great beyond.

Maybe they were. I'll let you make your own mind up.

It began in 1848. It was a night when clouds covered the moon, snuffing out its light, and a spring chill filled the air. Most people could be found kneeling by their bed, praying to God, and pouring their hearts out. However, the same couldn't be said for the Fox household. Inside the walls of their simple farmhouse, two sisters whispered and giggled with each other.

A secret was about to be shared.

'Kate. Maggie. What are you two conspiring about now? God hears all, you know? And don't you think that you should be asleep by now?'

Their mother, Margaret, inquired as she glided into the room so gracefully that it looked as if she was floating. The only giveaway was the sound of her heels clicking against the wooden floorboards underneath her long, sweeping dress. As a woman, she was the epitome of elegance who knew her place in society and carried herself with the knowledge that one day she would receive His judgement.

'Mother, how could we possibly sleep when we're so scared? There's something ... *otherworldly* in here and strange things have been happening. It's an ungodly presence I'm sure,' replied the eldest, Margaretta, with a smirk twitching at the corners of her mouth.

'Oh, honestly. You're speaking nonsense and I don't appreciate it.'

'It's anything but nonsense. It's the truth. You have to believe us, Mother.'

Eleven-year-old Catherine nodded eagerly along with her sister's words.

Their mother sighed. 'Very well. If you insist on this entertainment then please enlighten me on these strange happenings.'

The two sisters spoke over each other, their words colliding and jumbling in the air. 'The other night ... ' ' ... banging and ... ' ' ... something is ... ' ' ... they seem to be talking... '

'Girls, girls,' their mother protested, waving her arms signalling for them to be quiet. She rested her fingertips against her temples. 'One at a time, please.'

Margaretta spoke first. 'Kate and I were woken up the other night by banging and tapping.'

'It was so loud,' interrupted Catherine. 'And it was everywhere. On the walls. On the floors. On the bed. We didn't know what it was, and it was dark so we couldn't see anything.'

'We think they're ... it ... whatever ... is trying to talk to us. It seems to answer us.'

'And now it happens every night when we're sleeping!'

A silence followed as Margaret stood taking in all that the sisters were saying. The weight of their words seemed to tilt the scales of science and spirituality, of reality and religion ... of her own head and heart. Questions began to flood Margaret's mind, but they all evaporated before they could leave her lips.

'Show me.' Was all she could manage to conjure up.

With the two sisters huddled together on the bed, they began their demonstration.

'H-h-hello. Are you there?' Catherine's voice quavered.

TAP. TAP.

Their mother's hands flew to her mouth and chest as if someone was pulling on her puppet strings. All three of their eyes grew wide.

'D-do you kn-know wh-who I am?'

TAP. TAP.

'How m-m-many people ar-are in this roo-room?'

TAP. TAP. TAP ... TAP.

Catherine and Margaretta peered over at their mother to gauge her reaction. In the dim light, they could see her backed against a wall as she frantically completed the sign of the cross over, and over, and over.

'Our Father who art in heaven,' Margaret whispered pleadingly. 'God the powerful being, please offer us protection. God the all-knowing, please grant us answers and guidance. God the Holy Spirit, please show us mercy and compassion.'

Following their mother's lead, the sisters repeated her words of prayer and began blessing themselves. This, however, did little to ease the tightness in their chests as fear seeped into their skin and overwhelmed all of their senses. Shadows became dark figures. Flickering candle flames morphed into piercing eyes. Thudding hearts were mistaken for spiritual bangings.

Margaret tried to regain her composure. 'Count to fifteen,' she requested with a timid, barely audible voice.

The presence obliged by replying with fifteen taps.

She scanned the room looking for a culprit before sighing and giving up. Margaretta and Catherine sat quietly, happy that their mother believed them. She hadn't seen the string trailing from the sisters' hands to an apple core or heard their occasional sniggers, she only noticed the dull taps and the vibrations in the floorboards under where she stood.

'Are you an injured spirit?' Margaret continued.

The sisters pulled the string tapping the apple core against the floorboards twice for yes.

'Maggie. Kate. Look after each other, I'll be right back.' Their mother dashed out of the farmhouse and knocked on their neighbour's door.

'Margaret? What's wrong? You look like you've seen a ghost.'

'Close enough,' Margaret responded breathlessly. 'Follow me.'

Once the neighbour heard the tapping for himself, he quickly spread the word throughout Hydesville about the split-footed, devil spirit at the Fox household. One by one, everyone in the community visited the farmhouse to witness how the Fox sisters could communicate with ghosts. With the thumping of the apple core and the snapping of their fingers, Margaretta and Catherine turned even the sceptics into believers. The whole community was abuzz about this new religious movement that left no question unanswered – What waited for them after death? What was their life's purpose? Were their loved ones watching over them?

The final question everyone wanted answered was about the human entity that the spirit once was. It was after this discovery that Margaret decided it would be safer for the sisters to live with her other daughter, Leah. Except ghosts continued to communicate with them and Leah learnt she also possessed this ability. A simple prank had created this new reality that was now the family business, turning them into mediums and being catalysts for the world's spiritual awakening.

News of their gift developed until The Fox Sisters held their first seance in the biggest hall that they could find in Rochester. Four-hundred eager individuals swarmed in filling every seat as they patiently waited to see for themselves this mysterious phenomenon. Some were hopeful that they would hear from lost loved ones, others were just there to prove the whole thing as a farce. The anticipation in the hall was palpable as the three sisters walked onto the stage.

As moments passed, Leah, Margaretta and Catherine stood motionless letting an uncomfortable silence settle over the crowd. After various candles were blown out leaving the sisters in a cloud of darkness, they closed their eyes and held each other's hands as their audience continued to observe them with bated breaths.

'Are there any spirits with us this evening?' The sisters asked simultaneously.

TAP. TAP.

Gasps resounded throughout as spectators examined the room to find the source of the noise. This time, there was no string or apple core. There was no clicking of the fingers. There was no smoke and mirrors or added embellishments. Sceptics found there to be no sign of a hoax.

'What's your name?'

Using a communication tactic they had devised, the sisters started to recite the alphabet for the spirit to tap on the correct letters. They learned his name was Arthur White.

'That's my husband! That's my husband!' A woman in the audience wailed as she stood up from her seat and raced to the stage.

'Is that true, Arthur?'

Two taps answered.

'Do you have a message for her?'

Two more taps echoed around the hall.

Leah spoke the alphabet again allowing the spirit to tap until the whole message was known.

'Watching over you? Are you watching over her, Arthur?'

TAP. TAP.

As the seance continued, more audience members became emotional when their dearly departed made themselves known, and more messages were passed on. Everyone left there comforted and convinced.

In the years that followed, The Fox Sisters grew in popularity creating a community of dedicated spiritualists. Their lives became a series of seances and conversations with ghosts. Although there were many non-believers, there was never any proof of it being a hoax until one fateful day in 1888.

In that same hall in Rochester, Margaretta stood on the stage alone with her sisters in the audience. It was then that she told the world her truth.

'My name is Maggie Fox,' she began over a chorus of cheers and boos. 'Many of you are here because you know who I am and have been a part of the spiritualism movement my sisters, Leah, Kate, and myself created. As mediums, we were the first in the world to contact spirits, to have conversations with them, at least that's what we led you to believe ... For forty years now, we have been deceiving you all. The Fox Sisters are nothing more than a hoax. When it first started, I was too young to know how wrong it was, and it all grew out of control.'

Bewildered faces watched as Margaretta demonstrated her not-so-otherworldly abilities. Lifting up her dress, so that everyone had a clear view, she then cracked her toe joints against the wooden floor. A familiar tapping sound resonated throughout the silence of the hall as a fake seance was performed.

As the demonstration drew to a close, the final message of 'we will now bid you farewell' was tapped.

The Fox Sisters were done.

And this is where it ends, in 1893, where the truth will dissipate with my last breath. As I lay on my deathbed, Leah and Kate long departed from this world, little snapshots of my most important moments flash before my eyes. Of course, there are no moments more important than those with The Fox Sisters – from the prank to the seances to the false confession after the ghosts asked us to stop.

I wish we could do it all again.

I can hear my sisters' taps agreeing with me. I'm glad they think the same.

We were The Fox Sisters – Leah, Catherine and myself, Margaretta. Known worldwide, we were the most famous mediums of our age and the faces of Spiritualism. In a time when religion was rife, we were the ones that people turned to for comfort and answers about the mysteries of the afterlife. Everyone who saw us was so desperate to believe that it was true, that their departed loved ones were really sending them messages from the great beyond.

Maybe they were. I'll let you make your own mind up.

In the Silvery, Blue Void

Jeremy Dixon

Joe held the door still and slid around its edge, so that it didn't squeak on its dry hinges, holding his breath, feeling his way silently in the dark. He'd discarded his clothes on the landing and thrown them over the banister rail. He stood, shivering in his white cotton boxers, waiting for his eyes to acclimatise to what little light crept around the edges of the curtains. It was late and the house had slipped into the cold, dark hours. It felt alien – not like home anymore. Joe tiptoed through the room, across the grey woollen carpet to the bed, avoiding the loose floorboard in front of the wardrobe which complained noisily at the slightest pressure.

He'd been avoiding going to bed lately, until exhaustion had forced it – the lack of distractions scared him. He hadn't slept much since the funeral. It had surprised him, the questions which kept him awake. Will it now be him who is called upon to carve the Christmas turkey? And what about the Sunday joint of beef – if that tradition can survive, with a different head at the table. Who will nod knowingly when he next complains about the referee's eyesight? And will he ever be able to fix his car again? And ... and, what of his mum? Will she soldier on stoically, ignoring that half of her has gone? Or will she dwell on the missing part – wither and wilt, and lean on him like a crutch, when he was already struggling to support himself?

He peeled back the duvet and crumpled into the bed with an exhausted sigh. He touched his wife's shoulder, softly so as not to wake her. She needed her sleep. She'd been under the weather for the last couple of weeks, feeling nauseous and tired all of the time. He rolled over and closed his eyes and tried not to think.

Joe was drifting in the silvery blue light which filled the void between night and day. His eyelids flickered and his mouth twitched, his breaths long and slow. His hand, resting on top of the duvet, opened and then closed into a loose fist, as if it were squeezing another. Another that was strong and large, that wrapped tightly around his, and pulled him from the bed, from the room, from the house ... into the dream beyond.

He opened his eyes and could see the vague shape of the hand. Huge and fluid and engulfing his own completely. Long silver fingers writhed independently, like each had a mind of their own. They curled through his fingers and wrapped around his wrist, constantly moving, sometimes disappearing completely, only to reappear a moment later. They seemed to have no substance, like they were made of sparkling, silver smoke.

The hand was connected by a snakelike strand, thinner and much longer than a human arm, to a figure far taller than him. It held a shape, like that of a thin person, but only just, as if it might morph at any moment into something completely different. It was a swirling, curling, vortex of tone, black, then grey, and without warning, a dazzling silver, so bright that he was forced to shield his eyes. The figure was dragging him along some kind of curved corridor with no visible end and a ceiling which disappeared into a distant blackness. The ground beneath his feet was soft. It sapped his strength, like he was trying to run across a beach of dry sand. He began to pant as the muscles in his legs burned.

Stacked to each side of them were shelves of small golden jars, stretching higher than he could see. Each one emitted a soft amber glow like a child's night light. Without them, the corridor would have been in darkness.

Joe strained his neck as he ran, trying to make sense of his surroundings, trying to estimate the impossible number of golden jars. He supposed he should be scared, but he wasn't. There was something about the hand, clasped to his, something about the gentle but solid grip – a feeling of security perhaps, he wasn't sure.

'What are those?' Joe asked breathlessly.

The figure stopped and turned, and in the ever changing,

vaguely spherical shape where its head should be, were two sparkling, black orbs which he took to be eyes. Below them in the swirling silver smoke, a line appeared and seemed to curl upwards at its ends. Then it opened.

'Don't you know?' The figure's voice was soft like a warm whisper, deep but gentle. Joe couldn't tell if it was male or female, so he decided it was neither – it just was.

Without waiting for a reply, the figure turned and began dragging him again, faster than before. The twinkling jars whizzed by like strings of Christmas lights, until they became a fuzzy amber blur.

The figure stopped and turned again. The strange hand, entwined around his, evaporated away and reappeared wrapped around one of the jars. The figure lifted the jar and held it towards him.

Joe looked at the figure. It was darker now and the swirling vortices moved more slowly. The line of a mouth had gone. All that remained were the bright, black eyes, larger and darker than before. They shone like glistening pools of tar. There was a nod, which was more like a ripple, through the swirling grey mass.

He looked at the jar, took a deep breath and reached for it. As soon as his hands touched the cool, smooth surface, he could feel a familiar presence. He laughed, though he had no idea what at. He was a child again. He could smell the Blue Stratos aftershave which used to make him car sick when his dad overdid it. He could hear the tuneful, Cumbrian voice, 'tea-time Joe – come and get it, lad.' He closed his eyes, and he was running down the wing with the ball at his feet and his dad was jumping up and down, shouting instructions from the sideline. He laughed and sobbed as he gulped his next breath. A warm sensation soaked through his chest, his hands tingled, and his limbs suddenly felt weightless.

He pulled the jar to his chest and gripped it tightly, opening his eyes and staring at the shining black orbs. 'What is it?' he asked. The line reappeared and formed into a curling smile.

'Please, what is it?'

The figure lowered itself and leaned closer, so that it was nearly touching his face. 'Do you remember what you said? – at the funeral?'

Joe couldn't remember anything about the funeral. The whole thing was a blur, like it had happened in a dream or a nightmare or to someone else entirely. He shook his head, still clasping the jar.

'You said "they broke the mould",' the figure whispered, 'we didn't break it, we saved it, for when it's needed again.'

Joe frowned, running his hand across the surface of the jar. He held it close to his ear to see if it made any sound, then tried the lid, but it was too tight to turn. He lifted it, so that it was level with his eyes and peered into it, desperate to see more, to know more, and saw through the golden glass that the amber glow was a single small flame, flickering inside. He stared. 'That's him,' he said without looking away. 'Him,' the figure replied, 'and you, and all that came before and all that will come after.'

The figure held out a hand and gestured towards the jar.

Joe gripped it more tightly and shook his head, taking a step backwards, desperate to keep it. Strong, smoky tendrils appeared and wove around it, prying his fingers away from its surface. He watched as it was carried away and he felt unbearably alone again.

The figure placed the jar back in its place. Then it curled and twirled around and folded into him, and the voice this time was inside his head. 'It will pass,' it said, as if it could read his mind.

'Joe, Joe, wake up Joe.'

He groans and tries to open his eyes, but it's too bright so he only half opens them and squints through the tiny gap. The dream fresh in his head, he's surprised by the excited, feminine voice.

'Joe, wake up, I can't wait any longer.'

'What time is it?' His mouth is dry, his throat sore and his head heavy and full of cloud.

'Who cares? Wake up.' Sarah's on her knees, straddled across his chest. She has her hand on his shoulder and she's shaking him. The bed's squeaking on its old springs and the wooden frame creaks like it's about to collapse. He rubs his eyes, forces them open, and looks at her. She's grinning uncontrollably, and her blonde curls are falling forward, framing her face. She's waving a small, white plastic stick, squealing excitedly.

He reaches up and pushes her hair off her face.

'I'm pregnant, Joe – look.' She thrusts the stick into his face. 'We did it, we're going to have a baby.'

And he smiles because he knows that everything will be alright.

Thinness

Monica de Bhailís

from 'Two Houses: a Memoir'

I started to grieve for my mother long before she died. I was preparing myself for the loss of her for such a long time that I felt happy for her when she finally let go that night in late October. 'Well done, Mother', I called as the last breaths left her body. They hovered as a soft, high-frequency energy for several days in the room, the house, the yard and beyond, even after her body was taken away. I sometimes had to stop and listen; a sound like a tiny bell tinkled through the rooms, sometimes as if from outside a window, more often as if through a thin film of cloud or carried on the wind. Perhaps that energy came from inside myself: it felt right that she had a long, full life and that she finally died at home, in this house where she had lived and loved for almost sixty years. It also felt right to feel – or imagine? – her spirit about the place for several days, even weeks, after her death.

This was different. When other loved ones died, I only felt numbness – typically, I would disconnect from everything, including my own body and my physical surroundings. I was unable to feel anything until a quiet, private space would suddenly snare my trauma and hurl it and me into a dark pit where we would have to fight it out to the last. But Mother's death left the most remarkably tangible traces, and this was a revelation to me but also a kind of reminder, and a confirmation, of earlier experiences that I cannot explain. These experiences were unconnected to death – at least, as far as I was aware – but they also occurred in this place – in this house, and 'round about this house.

This place. This is a corner of Coolbrook. This is a large field, an orchard, small remnants of ancient woodland, a short lane turning into, then out of trees, onto a high lawn crowned by three enormous oaks framing an old house within their grand perspective. At the bottom of the field, there's a public road – it's been there for generations but we still call it the New Line – and, immediately beyond the road, the river running alongside it, about to make a tidy u-turn as it skirts the village. Along another side of our field, a back road connects to another back road that reaches the old Augustinian priory whose bells used to waft into our yard with Sunday morning breezes. Otherwise, beyond the patches of woodland, fields stretch out to the rest of the townland of Coolbrook, with its neighbouring farmhouse and lush fields of sheep and cattle, punctuated by seams of fine old trees.

This house. This house is Coolbrook Cottage. I should say, these houses. Coolbrook Cottage and its Gardener's House. Because I now know that the older stone building – standing behind what I think of as 'the house' – was also a habitation, and it predated the current dwelling house we call Coolbrook Cottage. Indeed, for quite a long time, the two houses co-existed as separate homes in what I will liken to a kind of marriage. A sloping yard – once gravelled, now cemented – keeps a short distance between them, holding them together – codependent, for better or worse.

Coolbrook Cottage and its Gardener's House. The former's 'cottage' denomination is misleading, for this is a sizeable old house, a cottage only by comparison to the grander 'big houses' from which many of its former residents originally came. The 'Gardener's House' label, suggesting former habitation by some better class of domestic servant, is also misleading, for in truth it was now an eyesore of an outhouse; where hens, cats and dogs lived, where tools, fuel, and all manner of paraphernalia and equipment were kept, whose windows were broken or boarded up and whose rotting stairs featured in the list of no-go areas we were warned against as soon as we were old enough to be cast outside in the morning and told not to come home until it was time for our dinner. A small room at the back was the cowhouse, where my mother milked two cows every morning and evening for decades, and this was where she came to me in the most vivid of dreams on one of those first nights after she died.

I'm lying in bed and I'm sure I'm awake but, there she is, milking a cow at the foot of my bed. Her back is towards me, a leaf-patterned headscarf leaning into the beast. Sweet smell of dung, the cow's heavy breathing, the hiss of milk filling and muffling the enamel bucket. I'm ranging around her: the texture of her teal-blue crimpolene skirt – I can touch it – then her calf high, grey-green wellies. Her hands, as I haven't seen them in many years – strong, working hands, the skin rough but the touch so kind and confident as she plays the cow's teats. I'm behind her again, sitting up in bed – I'm awake, surely? – and she turns around to look at me. She is younger and more beautiful than I ever remember her: many dark curls escaping her scarf tied under her pretty chin, her eyes shining and happy, her smile so entirely hers but deeper, truly delighted with me. I'm immersed in pure joy. My sense of joy for her, and of her joy in me as her child, was never surer. But I lose her in this observation. I'm now making my way through the woods, looking for her; I might just catch her before she leaves. The fellow in the rough serge suit and the bowler hat – the fellow I've seen between trees on a number of previous occasions and whom I recognise as 'the manager' – sees me and tips his hat to me, respectfully. I'm amazed. Not only have I never seen him in a dream before, or even in one-dimensional waking life before, but he's never acknowledged me in this way. Something must have changed. No sooner has this thought surfaced, I arrive at the bottom of the lawn, the house behind me. I'm looking towards the gate. A woman dressed in a smart riding skirt, coat and hat is leading a horse through the field-gap. The horse is magnificent, a lean, bay thoroughbred, hunter clipped, at least 17 hands; the woman looks slight beside high withers but she commands perfect control, embodies purpose. She looks towards me, momentarily, and I recognise her as my mother. She looks up towards the house, and I turn to follow her gaze. I'm surprised to notice the gable end of the Gardener's House is gleaming under a fresh coat of whitewash. I turn back towards my mother again; she's walking away from me, leading her horse – almost as if the animal were part of herself – around the turn in the lane, towards the gate.

And so, this dream and these thin days after Mother's death brings me back, back, back again to the Gardener's House. The image of the whitewashed gable wall stays behind my eyes, and I can't avoid thinking of another room in that building – the room we called the sitting room – into which I opened a door one day long ago, and witnessed something terrible. Something agonising that looked at me and screamed from a hole-mouth as it burned, melting, in unbearable red-heat and flames that leaped out and tried to snatch me into itself. I cannot have been more than 3 or 4 years old. I remember I wet myself in fright and horror.

Later, when I told, they said I must have imagined it, or made it up. This was my first, confused lesson in the twin realms of imagination and lies. A lesson in the difference between outside – so-called objective truth – and inside – the other life that is inside of my little body and my strange little mind. I'm told that what I saw – felt – is not actually real but that it's a lie that happened to me, and I may not have done it on purpose but I am responsible for this lie because I somehow created it. So it is like a sin, which I already know about, but I thought sins were reserved for my big brothers when they were disobedient or cruel. I become aware that I feel different now, having somehow taken a wrong turn. I'm very confused, ashamed and anxious.

When I got to the part in Hilary Mantel's memoir, *Giving Up The Ghost* where she writes of how she experienced a 'presence' one day in the secret garden, I cried my then middle-aged heart out. Perhaps wisely, she said almost nothing to describe that 'presence' – not even anything along the lines that it looked at her, or that there was a terrifying hole which was also a mouth, or a feeling of intense heat and flames. But she is clear her experience took place in an internal space, 'a waiting space cut out of my solar plexus' which she calls 'grace', or an expectation of God's arrival. But what came instead, she wrote, was something different, something very sinister: 'Sometimes you come to a thing you cannot write ... It wrapped a strangling hand around my life, and I don't know how, or what it was'. I cried because she could have been writing my life as a little girl, anxiously clinging to hopes of grace restored, trying to block out the horror, real or imagined, that I now knew existed.

Who knows what happened to me? Perhaps something so awful that I decided to forget the details and turn it into something else, more 'diffuse' – to use Hilary Mantel's word. Perhaps it was something innocuous that I somehow let into an internal hall of mirrors to be magnified and amplified out of all proportion. Perhaps I intuited or interrupted something that happened in the past, or even anticipated from the future. Perhaps it was all, or some combination of these things. Of course, I learned to live with it. The years taught me that the horror was not a lie I created: it didn't come from inside me, but it definitely belonged in Coolbrook.

let only my body rot down here

Soph Marlowe

a ghost walked over my grave

she dug her toes into the soft
summer grass collecting stains
as she knelt to my headstone

she clawed at the unforgiving dirt
desperate to remove it
to disrupt the smooth and lifeless
resting ground

she screamed and she wailed
the neighbourhood kids called her
the weeping woman wrapped in mist
and agonising despair

yet she couldn't hear them
she couldn't even see them
for she was too lost in her grief
to comprehend anything but her misery

stained and dishevelled by this endless spiral
she couldn't even understand the name
crying in the stone above
until she ran shaking fingers through the carvings

each letter sang a familiar shape
conjuring a word she recognised and dragged
from the pits of her fading memory

i walked over my own grave.

Last Will and Testament

Emily Jayne

I, the mother of creature and children
hereby declare this to be my will:

Find a hole, fit and ready in which my body shall be buried.
For I have no estate to divide.

To each and all my children I have already given
this corpse twice over: grown you, fed you, held you.

So when you lower me down – don't dress me.
I will go into the ground ready. Let worms and woodlice

writhe through my bones, my body a knot of roots.
Let my discharge replenish the soil

as I do not mind where the weeds grow –
let them bloom so the bees can find me.

Dance on my grave and leave no headstone
although you are prone to forgetting –

Leave me in the sweet-smelling earth,
and there I will recover.

The Tree Planters
Judy Smith

Here are the community-aware folk,
friendly, heads hunched together
or poised with forks and spades,
plastic sacks of canes, deer guards,
and lightly budded whips, labelled as trees
but with indiscernible identities,
to be holed and heeled
into chalk grassland
unturned for hundreds of years.

Caught on the soft spring breeze,
a rhythmic hum of chatter, laughter,
shared effort and flasks of strong tea.
We may be deluded about our impact
yet this keen scrawny lad
with tattoos and non-medical scars,
his open joy at this first tree planting,
confiding thoughts of his legacy
to some future, as yet unconceived, child,
his presence alone
tells me all will be fine.

Cassandra

Daren Schuettpelz

I watch her from the shadows of the long hallway. She stands before an open window as the warm breeze, the light, and the sounds from the street penetrate our flat. She's vibrating with anxiety but hiding it well. At least she thinks she is. I've known enough Cassandras to see the signs. The bitten fingernails and the grip on the Juliet balcony iron bars turning her knuckles white.

'You haven't told them,' I say.

'No, I haven't,' she replies, still facing the window. 'Not today, I think.'

I hear the coughing of lawn mowers chugging to life while children kick a ball in the street. From a distance, I catch a few notes from a cellist practicing for a performance. The notes dance and glide through the air. I choose not to look. I can imagine the soft yellows and pastels of the flowers young lovers give each other seeing eternity as a couple.

'Can you feel it?' asks Cassandra. 'Can you feel the breath of summer in this spring breeze? How nice it will feel to soak up the heat into our bones after such a cold and damp winter.'

'Not telling them isn't compassion, it's cowardice,' I reply, but it's as if we are having two different conversations. She remains at the window, staring down at the cacophony of life below us.

'I'll tell them tomorrow,' Cassandra says. 'Today is not the day the world should end. Let them enjoy their happiness. I'm breaking the pattern. Why should I warn them if they won't listen? Why tell them just to have them side eye me and whisper about how crazy I am?'

'You know that is not how this works,' I insist. 'I tell you and you tell them. They ignore you and are damned. That's how it always has been and how it will always be. You are not the only Cassandra, but *a* Cassandra. We know how this will play out. Ignorance isn't mercy. Why let them be happy when you know the extent of the pain and suffering plummeting towards them?'

'Because pain and suffering are plummeting towards them,' she whispers.

Mosaic

Isi Turner

One day, I won't exist.

I'll be an afterthought,
      a memory, a

             God I haven't thought about them in ages.

Until one day
you no longer think of me.

I will be erased from your life, left behind
Only in tiny mannerisms:
         Not stepping on pavement cracks
         But walking under ladders,
            And considering jumping on the next train,
         Just to go somewhere.

I know that you will erase me,

         slowly at first,

             then all at once.

Because all of my habits
Have been collected from the people of my past.

Contributors

Sharanya B is a poet who lives in Trivandrum, India. Her poems have been published/are forthcoming in *Tokyo Poetry Journal*, *Indian Literature* by Sahitya Akademi, *Santa Clara Review*, *The Wave* (Harvard), *Anthology of Poetry Society of India*, *The Madras Courier*, *Live Wire*, *Visual Verse*, *Boundless Anthology* (USA), *Unfolded Poetry Project* (USA), *Anthology of Tower Poetry Society* (Canada), and many other places.

Shamik Banerjee is a poet from India. He resides in Assam with his parents. His poems have appeared in *Fevers of the Mind*, *Lothlorien Poetry Journal*, *Westward Quarterly*, *Dreich*, and *The Hypertexts*, among others, and some of his poems are forthcoming in *Willow Review* and *Ekstasis*, to name a few.

Laura Beddow (she/her) is a nineteen-year-old writer and student originally from Staffordshire. Her writing has been enjoyed globally, by readers in over 110 countries. A self-proclaimed 'professional daydreamer', there is essentially little more to Laura than a boundless pen-wielder composed of big words and left-handed scribbles.

Sreelekha Chatterjee (she/her) is a short story writer, poet, researcher, and editor. Her short stories have been published in various magazines, journals, and have been included in numerous print and online anthologies. She lives in New Delhi, India. Facebook: facebook.com/sreelekha.chatterjee.1/, X: @sreelekha001, Instagram: @sreelekha2023

Laura Autumn Cox is a copywriter and editor based in York. She has written two speculative fiction novels and is currently working on a historical fiction novel set in the 10th century. Laura is the co-founder of York Writers, a collaborative space for local authors, poets, lyricists, and essayists.

Katie Day is based in the midlands, where she and her partner live on the top floor of a former 19th century asylum, though it is much less creepy than it sounds. She works in publishing and is currently working on a novel about an all-women cult.

Monica de Bhailís is a poet, researcher and writer based in Dublin, Ireland. She is currently working towards a first poetry collection with assistance from the Arts Council (Ireland). She is also writing a memoir based on her experience of growing up in a house with secrets linked to Ireland's troubled history.

Peter Devonald is winner of Waltham Forest Poetry, two Heart Of Heatons and joint winner FofHCS. Forward Prize and two BoN nominations. Poet in residence Haus-a-rest. Published extensively including *London Grip*, *Bluebird Word* and *the6ress*. 50+ film awards, former senior judge/mentor Peter Ustinov Awards (iemmys) and Children's Bafta nominated.

Jeremy Dixon holds a BA in English Literature and Creative Writing, and teaches creative writing night classes. His fiction has been published in the *Glittery Literary Anthology Four* and *York Literary Review 2023*. His stories have also appeared online with *Sky Island Journal*, *Loft Books* and *The Mocking Owl Roost*.

Peter J Donnelly lives in York where he works as a hospital secretary. He has been published in various magazines and anthologies. He was a joint runner up in the Buzzwords Open Poetry Competition in 2020 and won second prize in the Ripon Poetry Festival competition in 2021. His first full length collection *Solving the Puzzle* was published in 2023 by Alien Buddha Press, as was his chapbook *The Second of August*.

Anna Edwards is a MA Publishing and Creative Writing student at York St John University. Previously, she studied English and American Literature in Manchester. She is from the North East of England. Within this piece, she aims to capture the enlightening carefree spirit and confidence of many of the older women she has been in contact with in her life.

Daisy Edwards (she/her) is an autistic, bisexual writer. Last year, she was nominated for the Pushcart Prize by Arboreal Literary Magazine, and her work was featured by Carrion Press, Sunday Mornings at the River and Written Off Publishing. You can find her poetry in Issue 3 of Rooted Magazine. Instagram: @dredwards_writes

Ollie Groover (He/They) is a published American student from North Carolina studying Creative Writing at York St John University. They are a contemporary poet whose writing is heavily inspired by their experiences as a queer, trans person born and raised in the 'Bible Belt' of the American South. They aspire to help create societal awareness and empathy with their writing.

Ellen Harrold (she/her) is an artist, writer, and editor-in-chief of Metachrosis Literary. She uses painting, drawing, text, and textiles to explore physics and ecology through creative abstraction. She has recently published poetry in magazines such as *Shearsman*, *Die Leere Mitte*, and *Skylight 47*.

Holly Hartford (she/her) is currently in her second year of an English Literature degree at The University of York. After a childhood of unfinished stories and makeshift rhymes, the Durham-native started writing poetry in sixth form as a means of emotional catharsis – and hasn't looked back since.

Claire Huya (she/they) is a twenty-year-old Texan pursuing her Bachelor's degree in Creative Writing and English Literature at

York St. John University. When she can pull herself away from her countless stacks of books, Claire continues writing her fantasy novel while also dabbling in poetry and memoir writing.

Sarah Illingsworth is an avid poet, specialising in creative self-reflection. Her piece 'Balloon Love' was published in the 2022 anthology *All About Love*. She has recently graduated from Nottingham Trent University with a degree in Design for Theatre and Live Performance. She has a passion for Theatre, but her newfound love of teaching and children has led her to pursuing a career in teaching Art & Design.

Esta Innes-Limbachia (she/her) grew up in Leeds and is now raising her family there. She started writing poetry as a way of processing PTSD and post-natal depression. She was published in the inaugural Sisterhood anthology and performs her poetry across West Yorkshire.

Jack Jackson (he/they) is queer poet who grew up in Singapore and recently returned to the UK for university. He is the founder of The Poet's Society at the University of Lincoln and is planning on doing a poetry-centric MA. If he's not writing, he's probably daydreaming about space.

Emily Jayne (she/her) is a contemporary poet and fiction writer from West Yorkshire. She recently graduated from York St John University with Distinction in her Creative Writing MA. Emily has self-published two collections of poetry and enjoys finding unique ways to look at the world. Find her on Instagram @thatpoet_emilyjayne.

Grace Laidler (she/her) is a second-year student, studying film and television production. She currently lives in York, but is originally from South Shields. Grace regularly contributes to *True Faith* fanzine and writes a newsletter titled 'Grace About Town'. Her go-to karaoke song is Carly Simon's 'You're So Vain.'

Alexander Lunn is currently pursuing a postgraduate degree at The University of York. Between driving his Volvo across the Howardian hills, writing poetry and being a film/TV extra; he likes to explore all the world has to offer. But you're most likely to find him settling down, enjoying a beer, whilst watching the tide roll in at his hometown, Bosham.

Soph Marlowe (she/they) is a queer Yorkshire-based writer. She dabbles in poetry, memoir and screenwriting with themes of mental health, witchcraft, and queerness. By day, they're a Digital Copywriter and by night, a Creative Writing Master's student. They're a regular at Howlers, a poetry open mic. Her Instagram is @anotherpoet_soph.

James Rance is a York-based poet, performer and collage artist, drawing inspiration from Pagan spirituality, folk traditions and surrealism to create vivid sensory landscapes and an unsettling, dreamlike experience for the reader. His debut collection *Wheel of Light* was published in 2023 by Acid Bath Publishing.

Lucy Rumble is an emerging writer from Essex. Her poem 'My Nan, Remembered' won third place in the 2023 Tap Into Poetry contest, and her work has been published in *Crow & Cross Keys*, *Myth & Lore Zine*, and *Needle Poetry*, among others. Find her on Instagram @lucyrumble.writes or at lucy.smlr.uk.

Kummi Sandra (she/her) is a 22-year-old, Swiss-Mauritian poet based in Coventry. She has been published by Whimsical Publishing Press, Moonbow Magazine and Ukiyo Literary Magazine, and in *Beyond the Walls*. Having rediscovered her love of poetry in 2023, she is now working to publish and perform as many poems as she can!

Daren Schuettpelz (he/him) works as a teacher for US students in Germany and enjoys reading anything he can get his hands on and writing short stories in his free time. His work has found homes in several literary magazines and he was nominated for the Pushcart Prize.

Elliott Scriven is a twenty-four-year-old, York based writer from Newcastle Upon-Tyne. He is currently a student at York St. John university, studying an MA in Creative Writing. He has Cerebral Palsy and likes to write both poetry and creative non-fiction that represent the experiences disabled people live with on a daily basis.

Victoria Selnes (she/her) is a Norwegian writer and photographer living in Scotland. She has an MSc in Comparative Literature and fetches books for a living. Her writing has been published in *little living room*.

Brandon Shane is a poet, born in Yokosuka, Japan. He grew up in a small Okinawan village called Ogimi, where his influential grandfather worked a farm. You can see his work in the *Berlin Literary Review, Acropolis Journal, Grim & Gilded, Sophon Lit, Marbled Sigh, Verdant Journal* and *Remington Review,* among others. He would later move to San Diego, and graduate from Cal State Long Beach.

Judy Smith is an emerging poet. Since retirement she has been developing her writing craft with the support of some lovely online groups of poets. She lives in East Yorkshire and has a passion for gardening, wildlife and community tree-planting.

Rimika Solloway keeps a creative writing blog called *A Lack Thereof* (rimimonster.substack.com) and is part of the South East London Writers Group. She was born in Japan, raised in Orkney and grew up in London. A Bold Types 2020 Finalist for the Glasgow Women's Library, her work has been featured in *The Selkie, Potluck Zine* and other independent publications.

Elsie Taylor is currently a postgraduate student at York St. John University where she studies Creative Writing. Born in London on the edge of Richmond Park, nature has always been at the forefront of her writing whether that be through creative nonfiction, memoir or poetry. Before she began writing creatively, Elsie earned a bachelor's degree in Liberal Arts and this philosophical perspective continues to enrich her work with a sense of spirituality and wonder.

Charlotte Tunks is an aspiring author from York, currently studying an MA in Creative Writing and Publishing. She writes short stories inspired by folklore, ghost tales, and long winter nights. She is interested in the magical moments hidden within the mundane. Her work has been performed at York Theatre Royal, and she has co-written another piece, also performed at the venue.

Isi Turner (them/them) is a non-binary poet based in York. Their work leans into lyricism to create melodic poems that confront the complicated corners of the human mind, with themes of mental health and body horror. Their poetry appeared in The Palimpsest Literature Magazine. Instagram: @isiturner.poetry

Cheyenne Uustal (she/her) studied BA Creative Writing and MA Publishing at York St John University. You can find her other published works in *York Literary Review 2021 & 2022*, *Beyond the Walls 2022 & 2023*, Whimsical Publishing Press' *Seasons*, Bitterleaf Books *Fate*, Muttons & Nuts *Searching for a Sound* and on *Mindless Mag*.

Eleanor Walker (she/her) is curious and creative, always interested in bugs, animals, plants and sea creatures she might be able to discover when exploring somewhere, using crafts like textiles, drawing and writing to express her feelings and ideas. She is a primary school teacher-in-training and loves to share her excitement about the world with her class.

Emma Wells is a mother and English teacher. She has poetry and prose published with various literary journals and magazines. She is currently writing her fifth novel.

Lorraine Wood is a mature student who studied Creative writing at Liverpool John Moores University, then went to the University of Chester where she gained a Masters in creative writing. Poetry has been her main focus and has had work published in various anthologies. Lorraine is due to complete her Creative writing PhD at the University of Salford in the next few months. She has two grown-up children and a six-year-old grandson.